A NEW EARTH

The Jamaican Sugar
Workers' Cooperatives,
1975-1981

**Monica Frölander-Ulf
Frank Lindenfeld**

**UNIVERSITY
PRESS OF
AMERICA**

LANHAM • NEW YORK • LONDON

Copyright © 1984 by

University Press of America,™ Inc.

4720 Boston Way
Lanham, MD 20706

3 Henrietta Street
London WC2E 8LU England

Printed in the United States of America

Library of Congress Cataloging in Publication Data

Ulf, Monica, 1946-
A new earth.

Bibliography: p.
Includes index.
1. Sugar workers—Jamaica. 2. Sugar trade—
Jamaica. 3. Agriculture, Cooperative—Jamaica.
I. Lindenfeld, Frank. II. Title.
HD8039.S86J29   1985   334'.683361'097292   85-13546
ISBN 0-8191-4844-X (alk. paper)
ISBN 0-8191-4845-8 (pbk. : alk. paper)

TO THE JAMAICAN SUGAR WORKERS

TABLE OF CONTENTS

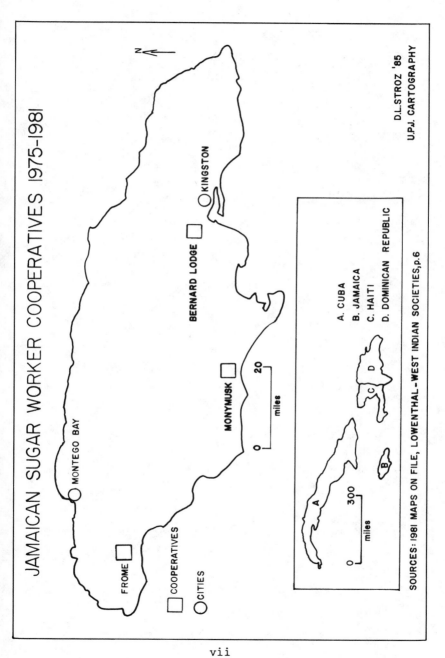

JAMAICAN SUGAR WORKER COOPERATIVES 1975-1981

MONTEGO BAY

FROME

MONYMUSK

BERNARD LODGE

KINGSTON

☐ COOPERATIVES

○ CITIES

0   20
miles

A. CUBA
B. JAMAICA
C. HAITI
D. DOMINICAN REPUBLIC

0   300
miles

SOURCES: 1981 MAPS ON FILE, LOWENTHAL—WEST INDIAN SOCIETIES, p.6

D.L. STROZ '85
U.P.J. CARTOGRAPHY

SAC organizer Joseph Owens

USWCC General Secretary
Winston Higgins (standing)
addressing workers at a farm meeting

Sandra Bingham

Clara Belle Gayle

Beryl Davis

Alexander James

Literacy class at Albany farm, Frome.

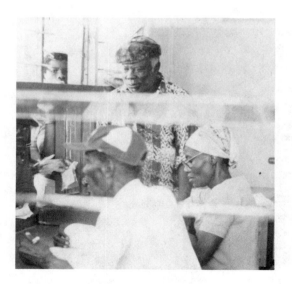

Sugar workers at Frome making up payroll
during the 1981 staff strike.

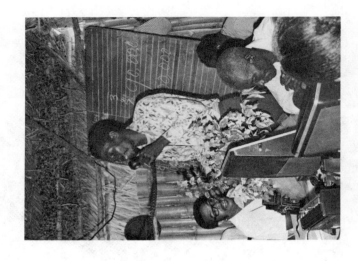

Matthias Brown addressing
a meeting of sugar workers.

Sugar worker spreading fertilizer.
(Note the fingers damaged from
handling the fertilizer).

Hauling cane to the Monymusk sugar factory

Billboard at the entrance to Barham farm, Frome.

Old sugar worker housing

And new...for a few

INTRODUCTION

This book tells the story of a movement to transform the oppressive social structure of three large Jamaican sugar plantations during the 1970's. It focuses on cooperatives organized among the 5,000 workers at the Frome, Monymusk and Bernard Lodge Estates on land formerly owned by two transnational corporations. The estates were divided into a number of farms, each farm covering 2,000 or more acres in cane. There were 23 farms in all, each with some 200 members, as well as service cooperatives for transport and irrigation. The cooperatives embodied a significant land reform and a major attempt to implement workers' control in Jamaica. Because of their size and their substantial contribution to the island's economy, these pioneering cooperatives held the promise of a model whose success might lead to widespread emulation and the eventual democratic-socialist transformation of the entire Jamaican society.

In the chapters that follow, we discuss the enormous difficulties faced by the sugar workers cooperatives and the numerous internal and external obstacles placed in their path. We believe that the very persistence of these cooperatives over six years was in itself a substantial achievement. And, the fact that a few farms showed a profit was quite remarkable. We trace the history of these cooperatives from the grass-roots organizing that began in 1973 while the reformist Peoples National Party (PNP) was in office, through their dissolution by the conservative Jamaica Labour Party (JLP) government in 1981. Our purpose is to analyze the strengths and weaknesses of this movement so that others may learn from their accomplishments and their mistakes and better understand the possibilities as well as the limits of democratic social reform.

In addition, we hope our book will help shed light on the issue of third world economic development. Large scale worker cooperatives represent a path to development different from that offered by capitalism and state socialism. The capitalist path, to which the incumbent Jamaica Labour Party government is committed, depends on substantial foreign investment and loans from the International Monetary Fund (IMF). The state socialist path as illustrated by Cuba has proven capable of reducing economic inequality, providing better medical care, increasing literacy, and making better use of productive resources, though it involves continued bureaucratic control of production from the top and single-party government, as well as continued reliance on outside help. In the Third World, especially in the agricultural sector, workers' cooperatives offer a viable alternative. They can provide the social and material basis for self-reliant economic development independent of the great powers, the transnational corporations and such international agencies as the IMF.

Because of their emphasis on bottom-up democracy and worker education, their potential for creating jobs and tapping latent reserves of worker initiative, creativity and productivity, workers' cooperatives seem well suited to advance economic development as part of a wider social and political movement. The potential of such a movement existed in Jamaica when the PNP was in power during the 1970's, especially after Prime Minister Michael Manley announced his party's commitment to democratic socialism in 1974. We were aware of the many attempts to promote agricultural producers' cooperatives in other countries, their partial success and the many disappointments, for example in Tanzania (1), Algeria (2) and Peru (3). The question was, would the Jamaican sugar workers' cooperatives prove to be different?

Although we were both generally informed about the reforms initiated by the PNP, neither of us knew about the Jamaican cooperatives until they had been in existence for several years. Because of Frank's interest in cooperatives and self-management, he attended the Fourth International Conference on Self Management in Atlanta, Georgia, during June 1978. There he learned about the Jamaican sugar workers' cooperatives from a talk given by Winston Higgins, the chief staff executive of the United Sugar Workers Cooperative Council (USWCC), the umbrella organization that united all of the cooperatives. At Higgins' invitation, he visited the three cooperatively-managed estates and secured agreement from the Central Board of the USWCC to return for a field study that began in summer 1979. The two authors met later that same year when Frank presented a paper about his preliminary work at a meeting of the Association for Humanist Sociology at the University of Pittsburgh in Johnstown, Pennsylvania, where Monica was teaching, and she

2

joined the study. As an anthropologist, she had long been interested in the Caribbean area and in the issue of third world development. Each of us traveled to Jamaica about half a dozen times for periods of three to six weeks between 1979 and 1982. Monica received some financial support and a sabbatical leave from the University of Pittsburgh, Johnstown; Frank's expenses were met by his personal funds.

Our original idea was to do participatory research in which we would engage in preliminary observation and analysis of the cooperatives and design a study with the help of the members which they then could use as a vehicle to help advance their own efforts. We visited many of the farms, spent time living among the sugar workers, observed and attended committee meetings, and tape recorded interviews with about two dozen members. The interviews were recorded at members' homes, at our residences, and at the work sites.

The cooperative organization consisted of two distinct groups, the cane workers and the staff. The staff, with the exception of the Member Service Officers, were not co-op members, but employees of the cooperatives and they were separated from the cane workers, i.e. the co-op members, by a wide gulf of social class and lifestyle. Even the language was different, in that the workers almost always used Patois, while many of the staff conversed with us in standard English. Among the staff, we spoke with top executives, member service and education staff, and a few of the middle managers.

We were unable to carry out our participatory research design for a number of reasons. The struggle between members and staff for control of the organization described in this book meant that outsiders such as ourselves were viewed as potential allies or enemies in the cooperatives' internal conflicts. The top executives were reluctant to support research with action implications, lest we disturb the organization's internal balance of power; our presence was actively opposed by some of the middle-level farm staff. Finally, the long time period needed to establish the necessary rapport with the sugar workers meant that by the time we were fully accepted by many of them, the new JLP government had abolished the co-ops. When it became clear in the fall of 1981 that

3

there would be no cooperatives to work with any longer, we felt we had an obligation to use what we had learned as best we could to document the sugar workers' struggle during the cooperative period. It is a small repayment for all the hospitality, kindness and trust we were shown by so many sugar workers.

The sugar estates are located in different parishes: Frome is at one end of the island in rural Westmoreland. Monymusk in Clarendon and Bernard Lodge in St. Catherine are about 100 miles away. We had intended to spend equal time on all three estates. Because of the lack of transportation which would have helped us move freely from one estate to another, the bulk of our research was actually done at Frome. Since Frank had begun his work at Frome, we developed the most extensive contacts there, leading to the arrangement of free accommodations for us at Shrewsbury farm and at the home of one of the education staff.

We defined our role as not merely impartial observers but as active participants willing to help further the progressive social and economic objectives of the cooperatives. We helped in some of the day-to-day activities of the education staff, such as participating in group discussions with the workers. Frank spoke with Managing Committee members (elected leaders of the cooperatives) at several Frome farms about crop diversification. He was able to provide some material help as well by donating an old VW bus to help transport workers to the education programs. (We had hoped the bus would also help us move around the island, but it was not in good enough repair for that). Frank also put the cooperatives in touch with the Philadelphia Quaker organization, Right Sharing of World Resources, which provided three grants totalling almost $10,000 to fund diversification projects.

Frank's initial contact with Winston Higgins, General Secretary of the central cooperative, the United Sugar Workers Cooperative Council (USWCC), provided us with an entry to the organization. At Higgins' invitation, Frank spoke about the research plans to the members of the Central Board of the USWCC (4) who subsequently agreed to the study and continued to help us throughout our stay. They welcomed us to any board meetings we wished to attend. As we were getting started, Higgins retired, and his position was

filled by E. B. Thompson, formerly chief staff executive at the Frome estate. The central office of the
USWCC included Thompson, Lennie Ruddock, Director of
Education and Training, and Glen Francis, Research
Officer. These three helped us gain access to the
organization's records and facilitated our data
collection.

At Frome, we worked closely with the education
staff, participating in discussions with them about
their plans and accompanying them to meetings and
classes. Often the teachers provided transportation
to the farms on the back of their Honda 50 motorcycles.

During two of her visits, Monica lived at the
home of one of the instructors, Sandra Bingham, in a
sugar worker community located next to a co-op farm.
Early in the study, Frank met one of the most dynamic
and outspoken workers' leaders, Matthias Brown.
Matthias was a former tractor worker who became a
cooperative organizer and was later promoted to Member
Service Officer. Over the course of several field
visits, we developed a warm friendship with Matthias.
Through his job he had contacts with workers at all of
the farms, and introduced us to many of them. Our
positive relationship with him served as a credential
that enabled us to attend meetings and gain the trust
of many cooperative members at Frome.

Our friendship with Matthias also labeled us as
progressive sympathizers. We had come to Jamaica to
study the co-ops because we supported their efforts to
build a better life for the sugar workers. We hoped
that Prime Minister Manley would find a way to implement his program of democratic socialism for Jamaica
as fully as possible, and saw in the cooperatives a
major step in that direction.

We freely admit to the bias apparent in our
study, which tells the story of the cooperatives from
a viewpoint sympathetic to the sugar workers, yet
critical of their mistakes (5). Our aim is to help
the cooperative movement by identifying the internal
and external problems encountered by the sugar workers' organization, and to point to lessons that may be
of help to others in establishing and maintaining such
cooperatives.

A consequence of our partisan approach was that we were welcomed by many of the sugar workers and by the progressive leadership of the Managing Committees and their allies who were Member Service Officers or teachers. This rapport enabled us to obtain permission to be present at and to record Managing Committee meetings.

Many staff members at Frome, however, perceived us as a potential threat to their power and their jobs. The more knowledge about the business and the more organizational skills possessed by the sugar workers and their leaders on the Managing Committees, the less dependent they would be on the existing managerial staff. As a result, the staff members were reluctant to consent to tape-recorded interviews. Some were quite uncooperative, sharing information such as payroll data only when ordered to do so by the top staff executives or the workers' Managing Committees. A few staff members even spread rumors designed to damage our reputation with the workers.

Despite such efforts to discredit us, our relationship with the sugar workers was very positive. This book could not have been written without their willingness to give freely of their time. While we lived at Shrewsbury, our neighbor was Alexander James, the Chairman of that farm's Managing Committee and formerly one of the members of the Central Board of the USWCC. We spent many happy hours talking with him. We are also especially grateful for the cooperation extended to us by the education staff, especially Donald Smith at Frome, Trevor Coleman and Marcia Williams at Monymusk, and to the members of the Managing Committees at all levels who consented to our being present at their meetings. We cannot begin to thank all of the sugar workers with whom we spoke, including Norma Brown, Cleaveland Dobson, Cecil "Police" Campbell, "Suk" Davis, Clarence Miller, Mendez Bacchas, Frank Morgan, Erna Blake, Clara-Belle Gayle, Beryl Davis and dozens of others. We gratefully acknowledge the help given us by the staff of the Social Action Centre (SAC) in providing background information, sharing photographs and the results of their studies with us, and for the lengthy tape-recorded interviews granted by Horace Levy and Jim Schecher. Former SAC member Joe Owens, whom we interviewed for two days while he was working in Florida, vividly brought to life the early organizing

6

period with its hopes and hardships. We thank him for his invaluable contribution. For helpful and incisive comments on earlier drafts of this book, we are grateful to Trevor Coleman, Carl Feuer, Frederick Fornoff, Horace Levy, Joe Owens, Gloria Rudolf, Jim Scofield, Michael Yates and Kathryn M. Lindenfeld. Our thanks also go to Dorothy Stroz for drawing the map, Linda Leech for making the graphs, and to Sandy Otte for preparing the manuscript for publication. We owe special gratitude to Matthias and Sandra whose trust in us helped assure us such a warm welcome by the sugar workers.

1. Michaela von Freyhold, _Ujamaa Villages in Tanzania_ (Monthly Review Press, 1979).

2. Ian Clegg, _Workers' Self Management in Algeria_ (Monthly Review Press, 1971).

3. Cynthia McClintock, _Peasant Cooperatives and Political Change in Peru_ (Princeton University Press, 1981).

4. The Central Board at that time included Stanford Phillips, Iseah Senior, Lloyd Vassell and Canute Hermitt from Monymusk; Cecil Campbell, Matthias Brown, "Suk" Davis and Alexander James from Frome; and George Parker, Dudley Hall and Frank Edwards from Bernard Lodge.

5. We would argue that all research dealing with social issues is partisan and that most so-called objective studies are biased in favor of those who hold power and against those working for structural change.

CHAPTER I

OUT OF THE PAST

> The sweetening of British tea has
> always taken priority over the filling
> of the Jamaican stomach. (Joe Owens)

For more than three hundred years, the best
agricultural land of the fertile Jamaican plains has
been planted in sugar cane. The sweat and toil of
tens of thousands of Jamaican women and men have been
expended on nurturing and reaping the cane to be
processed and shipped abroad, while they and their
children have suffered from debilitating poverty and
powerlessness.

The sugar plantation was for centuries central
not only to the British imperial economy, but to the
economy, political structure and the whole social
fabric of Jamaica as well. In the mid-1970's the
large sugar estates still accounted for about one half
of the total sugar cane production, and one half of
the value of all agricultural exports was derived from
sugar and sugar products. The plantation became the
symbol of oppression, exploitation and degradation to
all Jamaicans, a constant reminder of "slavery days"
and of the days of British colonial rule. In independent Jamaica, it revealed the continued economic and
social inequalities in the society: the descendants
of the slaves still worked in the fertile fields
producing sugar for others while their meager earnings
barely allowed them to fill their own and their
children's stomachs with food.

Thus the struggle to establish worker ownership
and control of the three largest sugar estates in
Jamaica in the early 1970's takes on particular
significance. It represented a momentous attack on
the plantation system by placing the land in the hands
of the workers and turning the rigid plantation
management hierarchy on its head, thus allowing the
sugar workers for the first time in Jamaican history
to work for themselves and to reap some of the fruit
of their labor. For some, the sugar cooperatives also
held the promise of a whole new Jamaica, self-reliant
and truly independent, with a democratically controlled economy serving the needs of the majority of
Jamaicans.

The sugar workers' struggle to gain control over
their own lives has a long history reaching back to
the first slave rebellions and the Maroon wars of the
17th century. It culminated in the movement to
establish cooperative ownership and control in the
sugar industry. To fully understand the place which
this recent period occupies in Jamaican history, we
must go back to the early days of colonial rule. We
must also look at Jamaican society as a whole, in
order to comprehend why, after many initial successes,
the cooperatives succumbed to outside pressures.

Slavery and the Sugar Plantations

Compared to any other area of the world, the
Caribbean region represents perhaps the most thorough
colonization by a European power. The original
inhabitants, the Arawak, were practically wiped out
within a century after initial colonization by Spain
in 1509. Diseases, rebellions and forced labor in
gold mines, on ranches and plantations took their
toll, forcing the Spanish to look for alternative
sources of labor. The first West African slaves were
brought in 1517; by the early 1600's, the slaves
slightly outnumbered the Spanish settlers in a total
population of about 1,500. Fewer than 100 Arawaks
remained. In 1655, Great Britain seized Jamaica from
the Spanish and embarked on an expansion of sugar and
tobacco cultivation in the West Indies. Although the
direction of Jamaican economic development was determined by the colonists and powerful economic interests
in the metropolis, the slaves, and later their descendants, continued to influence Jamaican culture and
society in major ways.

From the very inception of the slave system
Africans escaped from their masters and fled into the
rugged hills which form a ridge across the length of
the whole island interior. These were the so-called
Maroons (1), who set up their own communities and
lived by small farming and by raiding the plantations.
One such Maroon was Juan de Bolas, who at first allied
himself with the remaining Spanish, but eventually
joined the British in return for a guarantee of "all
the liberties and privileges of Englishmen" for all
the Maroons. The last Spanish survivors left the
island in 1660 and Great Britain became the sole
colonial power in Jamaica until its independence in
1962.

Initially soldiers, religious groups, indentured servants and convicts from Great Britain made their living mostly from farming subsistence crops and small amounts of cocoa, sugar and indigo for export. In the late 1600's several disasters hit the island: a hurricane, cocoa disease, an earthquake, a cholera epidemic and a brief invasion of French troops. The small farmers were forced to sell their holdings and slaves to wealthier planters and investors from England, leading to the development of large sugar plantations requiring a considerable number of slaves. As early as 1690 blacks outnumbered whites by four to one, and with the sugar boom of the early 1700's the ratio climbed to ten to one in 1740 and 12 to one in 1780.

> At that time (1780) there were about 200,000 black slaves in Jamaica, or more than a fifth of the total for the entire British Empire, and Jamaica was producing 50,000 tons of sugar a year, or roughly half of all British production (2).

The sugar boom continued until the early 19th century. In 1815 Jamaica was producing 79,660 tons of sugar, using more than 300,000 slaves who constituted almost 86 percent of the total population. The white population of about 15,000 represented only 4.4 percent of the island's population, while the free colored, or people of mixed African/European ancestry, constituted about 10 percent of the total (3).

Today it may be difficult to fully appreciate the importance of sugar produced by West Indian slaves to the British economy and political organization two centuries ago. The sale of slaves became very lucrative to Great Britain. Craton has estimated that the slave trade brought in average profits of about 16 percent on invested capital for the whole slave-trading period. The Jamaican sugar plantations may have brought as much as 20 percent profit before 1700 when land was still very cheap. Sugar profits averaged 10 percent in the mid-1700's compared with 7.5 percent at the end of the century (4).

11

Adam Smith wrote:

> The profits of a sugar plantation in any of our West Indian colonies are generally much greater than those of any other cultivation that is known either in Europe or America (5).

The sugar plantation system did not only create direct benefits in the form of profits to its largely absentee owners in Great Britain, but also had enormous indirect benefits in profits and employment in tangential activities such as sugar refining, rum distilling, shipbuilding, manufacturing, banking and insurance (6). Jamaica and the other British West Indian colonies were to produce raw sugar only. It was then sent abroad to be processed and refined. At least two-thirds of the profits left the islands, while the shipbuilding and manufacturing industries as well as commercial institutions provided fuel for the industrialization and economic development of England. The people who formed the backbone of this development, the slaves in the West Indies and the workers in England, had no power to control the wealth created by their labor. The West Indian planter and merchant classes had formed a powerful lobby in the British parliament which put up determined resistance to any policies aimed at breaking up their trade monopoly, including an increase in the sugar duties, abolition of the slave trade, or emancipation of the slaves.

In Jamaica and the other British colonies in the Caribbean, a small upper class composed of planters and merchants used the courts and the local legislatures to perpetuate their power. First-generation planters were generally not wealthy enough to revisit England, but sent their sons to be educated there. Later generations would prefer what they considered to be a richer cultural milieu of the metropolis.

By the middle of the 18th century absenteeism had become the rule, and the majority of plantations were in the hands of overseers, attorneys and bookkeepers. Craton describes them as "an embattled, embittered class with few inner resources to resist the temptations of petty tyranny or the trauma of alienation from work or work places to which they had little personal attachment" (7). They formed a small imperial middle class.

The vast majority of the population, the slaves, worked on sugar plantations. A medium-sized plantation of about 1,000 acres of land with 300-400 acres planted in cane, required about 400 slaves and approximately 175 head of cattle. Throughout the 18th century, until the abolition of the slave trade in 1807, the proportion of Jamaican slaves born in Africa was over 50 percent of the total slave population, since the planters generally found it cheaper to buy new slaves than to try to augment their slave population through a natural increase. The harsh conditions on the estates, the lack of immunity against epidemic diseases, the high ratio of males to females especially in early slavery were main factors contributing to high mortality rates and low fertility rates in the slave population. Of those Africans who managed to survive the brutal hardships of their journey across the Atlantic Ocean, about one third died during the first three years of work on a sugar estate.

Sugar cane cultivation required a large slave labor force mainly because of the need to harvest the mature cane rapidly, in order to maintain a high juice content. The fields were planted in rotation and were harvested one after the other through the five- or six-month harvest season. During the rest of the year, in the off-crop season, most of the planting, weeding, fertilizing and the digging and cleaning of drainage ditches was done. The field slaves were divided into gangs according to strength and ability: the largest gang, called the Great Gang, was composed of adult, able-bodied workers, male and female. Weaker adults and youths were organized into the Second Gang. Children, some as young as 6, were members of the Third Gang which was responsible for the weeding and manuring of the fields. The gangs were supervised by headmen, or drivers, appointed by the overseer from among the ablest slaves. These and skilled workers, such as the boilers, coopers, masons, carpenters, blacksmiths, head cattlemen, and watchmen composed the "elite"group among the slave labor force. On some large estates the majority of the field labor force was female, while most of the skilled jobs, with the exception of housekeepers, nurses and midwives, were held by men (8).

The slaves were worked from before dawn to dusk, six days a week, a little over 300 days a year. Even in the out-of-crop season they were called to work

13

12-14 hour days, maintaining the fields, to keep them out of "dangerous" idleness. On Sundays, they were expected to tend to their provision grounds, which were instrumental in providing them with the bulk of their food, consisting of yams, sweet potatoes, bananas, plantains and cassava. For protein most slaves had to depend on small rations of imported salted codfish or pickled herring.

> At best - where masters were compara-
> tively generous with issues and slaves
> were given sufficient time and ground
> to grow their own provisions - the
> slave diet was barely adequate; mono-
> tonous, starch-heavy, and deficient in
> protein and vitamins...In times of war,
> hurricane or exceptional drought,
> actual starvation was not unknown (9).

The long and hard work hours, often in heavy rain or in broiling sunshine, coupled with a meager and poorly-balanced diet contributed to a generally low level of health among the slaves. Diet-related illnesses, pulmonary infections and fevers, smallpox, measles and yaws, among others, were all quite common in the slave population, which added to their hard-ships.

Slavery has been legally defined as the "status or condition of persons over whom any or all of the powers attached to the right of ownership are exer-cised" (10). In Jamaica, the people who ruled and made the laws were the planters who were also slave owners. As a result the laws protecting the slaves were few and seldom enforced, especially in the early slavery period. After it became clear to the planters that the abolition of the slave trade was inevitable, some efforts, motivated by self-interest no doubt, were made to improve the conditions of the slaves. For example, somewhat more severe penalties were imposed on masters who wantonly killed their slaves. No slave could testify against a white person, how-ever, and the planters retained absolute legal power, often abusing it. In the two decades preceding the abolition of slavery, the planters returned to merci-lessly wresting a maximum of labor from their slaves. Punishment of slaves was extremely brutal. According to a pro-slavery observer, the usual punishment for rebellion was:

> Burning them by nailing them down on
> the ground with crooked sticks on every
> limb and then applying the fire by
> degrees from the feet and hands,
> burning them gradually up to the head,
> whereby the pains are extravagant...
> For crimes of lesser nature Gelding, or
> chopping off half of the foot with an
> ax...For Negligence, they are usually
> whipped by the overseer with lance-wood
> switches, till they be bloody, and
> several of the switches broken, being
> first tied up by the hands in the
> Mill-House...After they are whipped
> till they are raw, some put on their
> skins pepper and salt to make them
> smart; at other times their masters
> will drop melted wax on their skins and
> use several exquisite tortures...(11)

The slave laws also became increasingly racial in
tone. In 1696, the penalty imposed on a slave for
striking a white person was death or any other punishment deemed appropriate by the judge. Earlier the
same law had read Christian and later white Christian.
As was the case with slaves, evidence against a white
person by free Black people was not accepted by the
courts.

> In Jamaica the Negro race had become
> identified with slavery and this was
> the basic assumption of all its law
> (12).

Slaves did manage to gain certain customary
rights, however, which the planters often respected.
These included the right to use some land for provisions, a house, and some goods (except horses and
firearms), although slaves could not legally own
any property. Slaves were usually consulted before
they were sold individually to a new owner, so as to
prevent them from becoming habitual run-aways, although a master could legally sell a slave at any
time. The very conditions which made slavery particularly brutal in Jamaica, i.e., the absence of a strong
state apparatus and social controls and the high
degree of absentee ownership of plantations (resulting
in a very small white population), also gave slaves
the opportunity for a wide variety of unsupervised

15

activities outside the work situation, activities which often transgressed the laws yet remained undetected. Those slaves who survived the brutality of the system did so by varying degrees of accommodation to the slave system and, above all, by creating a world of their own, adapting African village traditions to the requirements of plantation life. Respect or high status were derived not only from traditional African activities such as healing, spiritual leadership, music, storytelling, clowning, carving, weaving and midwifery, but also from the plantation-related activities such as headmanship, skilled crafts and domestic work. Although in the alien world of plantation labor the slaves were stripped of their humanity, driven like cattle in the fields or in the boiling house, sold to a new owner, whipped for the slightest transgression, they would assert their humanity and individuality in their relationships with each other and in their response to their oppression.

Out of this struggle to remain human and to survive, a rich cultural tradition emerged which blends African and also European cultural elements that provide the basis for present-day rural Jamaican society.

Slave Resistance

Opposition to slavery and the plantation system runs like a blood-red thread through Jamaican history. The continuous imports of new African slaves throughout the 18th century fueled resistance against the harsh and inhuman conditions imposed on the plantation slaves. Opposition was expressed in a variety of ways: by feigned sickness, work slowdowns, careless work, deliberate destruction of tools and plantation property, pilfering, arson, murder, escape, full-blown rebellions and the Maroon Wars.

Until the mid-1700's, the Maroons constituted a major threat to the planters and the whole plantation system, given their constant attacks and raids on estates and their provision of a haven for runaway slaves. In the early part of the 18th century the so-called Leeward Maroons, a group of runaway slaves lead by Cudjoe, had been formed, and another band was becoming influential in the Blue Mountain region of the Northeast. Between 1725 and 1740, an all-out war against the Maroons was launched by the British militia. A woman named Nanny (now a national heroine of Jamaica) led the struggle at Nanny Town, a Maroon community attacked and eventually destroyed by the British army. In a famous trek, Nanny then led her band to the west to join with Cudjoe's forces. Cudjoe eventually agreed to a peace treaty with the British, which guaranteed him and his people freedom, 1,500 acres of land and the recognition of Cudjoe as the leader of his community for life. In return he agreed to cease the attacks on British plantations and promised to return runaway slaves.

More rebellions followed, such as the one in 1760, which resulted in the deaths of some one thousand slaves and 60 whites. This rebellion lasted for six months until the leader, Tackey, was killed by the militia.

Toward the end of the eighteenth century, Jamaica started to lose its position as the hub of British imperialistic interests. The British colonies in North America were threatening to buy molasses from non-British colonies such as St. Domingue at cheaper prices. The independence of the North American British colonies in 1776 represented the final blow, seriously undermining Britain's monopoly on the trade with its West Indian colonies. The focus of British trade now shifted to India and cotton production there. The Jamaican plantation owners found themselves in serious financial difficulties, and many ended in bankruptcy. But the real losers were the slaves. Thousands died as a result of starvation, diseases, deprivation and ill-treatment. These brutal conditions and the successful revolution in Haiti spurred more resistance among the Jamaican slaves. A second Maroon war erupted in 1795; in 1831, slaves in the Montego Bay area rose up in a major revolt, burning 160 properties and killing a dozen whites. About 400 blacks died in the fighting, and some 100 more were executed.

Emancipation

Freedom from slavery finally came in 1838 when declining sugar production, the abolition of the slave trade in 1807, an increasingly vocal abolitionist movement in England and the Montego Bay uprising had convinced enough of the members of the British House of Commons that slavery was no longer in the interest

17

of the British empire. The planters tried, unsuccessfully, to assert their independence from England, but
were granted only some measure of local control. The
decline in sugar production continued, however, as a
result of slumping sugar prices following the repeal
of the preferential sugar duties in 1847 (13). The
freed slaves left the plantations in the thousands to
settle in the mountains or on abandoned estates.
Jamaica was ideally suited for this development of an
independent peasantry.

> In 1838 probably no more than half the
> cultivable land had ever been put to
> use, and perhaps a quarter of the sugar
> lands had already fallen out of culti-
> vation. Between 1840 and 1845 alone
> the number of holdings over 1,000 acres
> fell from at least 755 to about 650,
> while at the same time the small
> holdings of under 10 acres increased
> from about 900 to well over 20,000.
> ...by 1854, when only 330 sugar estates
> remained, as many as 300,000 Jamaicans
> were being supported by peasant farming
> (14).

In the new villages, the people cultivated small plots
of land, growing basic provisions such as yams,
bananas, dasheen and sometimes sugar cane and other
cash crops for sale. Some, who only produced enough
for their basic food needs, would also look for work
on nearby estates, or come down from the hills to work
during the sugar harvest season. Although the freed
slaves were no longer bought and sold as cattle, and
although they were no longer under a harsh plantation
regime, their lives continued to be tied to the
decline or prosperity of the sugar industry. For
most, life remained full of hardships. Those who had
to supplement their small farming by estate labor were
now competing for such jobs not only with a rising
black labor force, occasioned by the doubling of the
Jamaican population in the nineteenth century, but
also with imported Indian indentured servants, over
whom the planters had a greater degree of control.
Numerous taxes were imposed on the peasants, such as a
house tax, a land tax and sales taxes. The "higglers"
(peasant traders) were prosecuted if they did not buy
a license; local magistrates often harassed people for
petty offenses; waves of squatter evictions occurred

any time an owner wished to reassert his claims. Even though the burden of taxation fell disproportionately on the peasants, practically nothing was done to improve roads, education, sanitation and health services in the rural areas. Some efforts were made, for example by George W. Gordon, a colored member of the Jamaican Assembly, to challenge the power of the local planters and merchants and the control by the British over local Jamaican conditions by pushing for extended suffrage rights for small farmers. Most Jamaicans, however, remained without a voice in local or national politics. The effort to evict a number of squatters from three estates in St. Thomas-in-the-East resulted in an uprising, led by a Jamaican Baptist minister, Paul Bogle. The courthouse in Morant Bay was set on fire and close to 20 whites and blacks, including three particularly hated planters, were killed by the rioters. Colonial troops were dispatched and the uprising was put down quickly and brutally. Paul Bogle and George Gordon, among others, were hanged. All in all, over four-hundred black Jamaicans were killed, some six-hundred were publicly flogged and over one-thousand peasant homes were burned to the ground.

The British saw the revolt as proof that the planters were not able to properly administer the colony and proceeded to dissolve the Jamaica Assembly and institute Crown Colony, or direct British, rule. The planter class did not fight this move by the British, but preferred to continue a humiliating colonial relationship rather than face the growth of real democracy in Jamaica. Political leadership slowly passed into the hands of the intermediate colored group, pro-British and pro-white, who were unable to develop a genuinely nationalist consciousness. Although a few black Jamaicans began to enter civil service positions (in addition to serving as teachers and ministers, the two professions which previously had provided a training ground for black leadership) the class and color hierarchy remained fundamentally intact until independence.

Enter the Transnational Corporation

The late nineteenth century saw the beginning of what was later to become a considerable corporate and North American involvement in the Jamaican economy. Sugar exports were increasingly going to the United

States because of price competition from beet sugar produced in Europe. By 1910 the United Fruit Company plantations nearly monopolized banana production, much of which was originally in the hands of small peasant producers. The United Fruit Company became powerful enough to run its own candidates in local elections. By 1930 the company owned not only plantations, but shops, shipping companies, wharves and hotels. Other corporations, such as the British-owned Tate and Lyle Co., were buying up sugar estates. In 1937, West Indies Sugar Company (WISCO), a subsidiary of Tate and Lyle, bought up seven of the remaining thirty-five sugar estates on the island. WISCO also brought factory centralization, mechanization of some operations, primarily transport and loading of the cane, and new cane varieties.

Unable to compete with such giants, the small farmers were gradually forced off their holdings and back to the plantations or into the city in search of work. Unemployment, malnutrition, hunger and disease were rampant. A report of the West Indies Royal Commission of 1937-38 catalogues the ills of the West Indian sugar colonies: a declining sugar industry with a highly exploitative task work system and a wage level as low as a hundred years earlier, gross malnutrition and chronic sickness, decrepit, unsanitary and overcrowded housing, a working-class in a state of economic servitude to a well-organized employer class, stultifying anti-union legislation, an extremely low status of women and children, and an obsolete and understaffed educational system. The meager wages were often further reduced through arbitrary punishments for even minor infringements. The late Clara-Belle Gayle, a former sugar worker at Frome estate, remembers "Charlie's days":

> We used to work in the factory, four of us women. We usually got 4sh. 6p. per week and if one woman came late they took 2sh. 6p. In those Charlie's days you have men who drove cow carts and the staff master was so wicked that a man who worked at L1 3p, (a week) and drove a cow cart and brushed the cart against the gate had to pay L1 and the task master only gave him 3p. So the man had to go back and borrow from him.

Such conditions continued to spark resistance among the Jamaican working people.

The period between the two world wars saw a proliferation of organizations attempting to gain more access to the political process. A vibrant trade union movement was beginning to develop under the leadership of A.G.S. Coombs. Marcus Garvey called for land reform and political and legal justice, and attacked white supremacy and colonialism by advocating unity of all black people and "Africa for Africans". Garvey also founded a political party and a trade union. By the late 1930's, protests and strikes flared up all over the island; in 1938, the unrest culminated in major riots, which marked a turning point in Jamaican politics. The riots began at Frome, a WISCO-owned sugar estate. The strikers were joined by hundreds of unemployed people who had not been among the one thousand just hired by WISCO. The police were called in by the managers; in the resulting conflict four strikers were killed, nine were wounded and eighty-five arrested. This event was followed by more protests and strikes. On one occasion, some two hundred stevedores employed by United Fruit Company and a group of militant banana workers brought the whole banana industry to a halt. A general strike in the capital, Kingston, brought the city to a stand-still.

Out of these riots rose two new leaders, Alexander Bustamante and Norman Manley, who were to dominate Jamaican politics for the next two decades. Alexander Bustamante, the founder of the Bustamante Industrial Trade Union (BITU) and the Jamaica Labour Party (JLP) was a charismatic leader enthusiastically supported by the great majority of Jamaican workers. He was primarily concerned with improving the economic conditions of the workers and defending them against the planter class while at the same time he supported a free enterprise economy and British imperial domination. Norman Manley, a lawyer, organized the People's National Party (PNP) with mostly middle-class professionals, lawyers, doctors and teachers, in leadership roles. The PNP advocated universal suffrage and the end of Crown Colony rule, which was to be replaced by a democratic socialist Jamaican controlled government. In the first elections of the first wholly elected House of Representatives in 1944, Alexander Bustamante emerged victorious.

Post-war Jamaica

After the second world war, the power of Great
Britain was greatly weakened. The United States
became increasingly important in the Caribbean and
Latin American. It favored independence for Jamaica
as a way to strengthen its economic foothold over the
island and the region. The Cold War between the
United States and the Soviet Union also had its effect
on Jamaican local politics: People's National Party
officials purged left-wing party members, who had
organized the Trade Union Congress (TUC), and in 1952,
TUC was replaced with a more moderate union, the
National Workers' Union.

While these political developments were taking
place, the economy remained stagnant and heavily
dependent on exports of plantation crops. Agricultural products accounted for 87.5 percent of all
exports in 1946, but at the same time over one-third
of locally consumed food, drink and tobacco had to be
imported. Thousands of rural workers and displaced
farmers were migrating to the cities in a desperate
search for jobs and economic opportunity. In the
hopes of diversifying the Jamaican economy, the
Jamaica Labour Party (JLP) embarked on an industrialization-by-invitation program, offering tax holidays,
cheap land and a large and low-paid labor force to
prospective foreign investors. This program particularly benefitted a number of North American aluminum
companies, which by 1957 had made Jamaica the world's
largest producer of bauxite.

The changes in the economy were accompanied by
the gradual replacement of the formerly ascendant
planter class by upwardly-mobile representatives of
manufacturing and commercial interests as the dominant
sector of the upper class. The new elite tried in
1944 to exert direct political power through their own
party, the Jamaica Democratic Party, but lost miser-
ably at the polls. Instead, they began to make
inroads into the other two parties and were able to
gain influence through financial support and through
appointments to statutory corporations and boards and
executive government positions. The two main parties,
the JLP and the PNP, were becoming increasingly
similar in their policies, if not in rhetoric and
symbolism.

22

> After 1952, when the PNP expelled its
> left-wing, both parties ceased any
> pretence they may have had to being
> genuine popular parties...(15)

Both parties were dominated by the middle and upper
classes. The PNP, after coming to power in the 1955
election, continued to invite foreign investment into
the island in the hopes of spurring economic development.

In the meantime, Great Britain was trying to
bring all of the British Caribbean into a federation.
This sparked an intense debate in Jamaica between
Norman Manley and the PNP, who supported the idea of
the federation, and Alexander Bustamante and the JLP,
who opposed it. The proposal to create a federation
was eventually defeated in a referendum in 1961, but
the debate had diverted people's attention from the
issue of independence for several years. It was not
until 1962 that Jamaica was finally granted independence by Great Britain. Independence implied no
significant changes in economic policy, however.
Alexander Bustamante was elected the first Prime
Minister of independent Jamaica, and his party, the
JLP, continued to pursue the established development
strategy, a Jamaican version of Puerto Rico's Operation Bootstrap. Generous tax holidays, duty-free
entry of imported raw materials and spare parts for
the manufacturers, unlimited remittance of profits to
corporate headquarters overseas and investment in an
infrastructure necessary to support the new industries
were offered as lures to foreign capital. Most of the
foreign investors who responded favorably moved into
the tourist industry, the manufacture of import
substitutes and goods for export and, above all,
bauxite. Of some one-billion ($U.S.) invested by
about 120 American companies in a twenty-year period,
700 million dollars were invested in bauxite. The
industrialization-by-invitation model of development
kept foreigners in firm control of the majority of
economic activity on the island, just as they had been
when the sugar plantations dominated the economy.
Increasingly, however, the British monopoly was
broken, and Jamaica came to rely on investment from
North America (mainly the United States) and on
international financial institutions such as the World
Bank and the International Monetary Fund (IMF).

By the late 1960's all the bauxite mining, three-quarters of all manufacturing, two-thirds of all financial institutions and of transportation, over half of communications, of warehousing and of tourism and two-fifths of the sugar industry were owned by non-Jamaicans (15). The bauxite industry and infrastructural development in turn created auxiliary industries, such as cement and construction, which were controlled by a handful of merchant and land-owning Jamaican families, the so-called twenty-one families. All of these families are of English, Syrian, Jewish or Chinese descent in a country where the vast majority of the population is black or brown. Although winning the right to universal suffrage had paved the way for potential acquisition of power by the black and the brown sectors of the Jamaican population, after independence the power of the economic elite was in fact strengthened through its access to top administrative and executive positions in the government.

In the Jamaican countryside the struggle over land and control over agricultural production continued between the large sugar estates and the small independent farmers. Between the two world wars, the sugar industry experienced some major changes. Two transnational corporations, the American United Fruit Company and the British Tate and Lyle Company, bought up a number of sugar factories and the surrounding cane lands. They then initiated a process of centralization and modernization of factory operations, introduced new cane varieties and increased chemical fertilization, which led to larger factory output and greater cane yields. The number of sugar factories in Jamaica decreased from 74 in 1910 to 26 in 1944, while average factory output increased from 288 tons per year to 5,842 tons per year in the same period (17).

The small-farming population mushroomed in the first half of the twentieth century and was increasingly drawn into cultivation of export crops, especially bananas and sugar. The large-scale central factory system encouraged the growth of the small commercial farming sector in order to ensure a steady, sufficient and cheap supply of cane to the factories. The small farmers thus came under the direct control of the factory owners, who could regulate their production and the price of cane in return for accepting good quality cane from the farmer. Producers' associations were formed, the Sugar Manufacturers' Association, a very powerful organization of the estate owners, and the All Island Jamaica Cane Farmers' Association, in which the large-scale commercial independent farmers dominated a majority membership of small cane farmers. The commercialization of small farming proved beneficial for a few; many, however, became victims of soil erosion, taxation of land, fluctuating prices and production and expensive farm inputs such as equipment, fertilizer and herbicide. These factors reversed the earlier trend by forcing many small farmers out of cane farming. Between 1965 and 1975, private farms (other than the estates) continued to grow about half of Jamaica's cane. But their number declined from about 28,000 to 14,000, and production was increasingly concentrated in the hands of the larger landowners. In the same period, the three largest sugar estates, Frome and Monymusk, owned by WISCO, and Bernard Lodge, owned by United Fruit Company, increased their share of cane production from about 23 percent to 30 percent of the island's total.

On the estates the majority of sugar workers lacked access to farm land. Marginal estate lands, even swamp lands, were increasingly taken into sugar production, or were left unused by the sugar companies. The post-war sugar boom, which was reflected in the tripling of sugar production between 1943 and 1954, and which in 1965 peaked at 500,000 tons of sugar, resulted in migration to the estates and population centers on the sugar plains. With little or no land to cultivate subsistence crops, the cane workers were forced to buy most of their basic necessities. Meanwhile the small farmers were diverting more of their production from food crops to export crops, which resulted in higher priced domestically produced foods. This in turn limited the markets for these crops, since fewer people could afford to buy them in sufficient quantities.

What made the lot of the sugar workers even worse was the seasonality of work in the sugar industry. Estate employment provided only occasional work on a task basis, even during the crop season. When the task was finished, the employer was under no obligation to provide more work or even to give notice of dismissal. Some improvements were achieved, however, mainly as a result of rising sugar production and the militancy of the sugar workers. After the 1938 riots, this militancy found organized expression primarily through the BITU (Bustamante Industrial Trade Union) and to a lesser degree its rival NWU (National Workers' Union). Wages rose significantly after numerous work stoppages in the early post-war period and continued to rise until the 1960's. But again the trend was reversed, and for the next ten years the workers faced declining incomes (18) as well as massive lay-offs.

The Declining Sugar Industry

The lay-offs were the result of a continued effort by the estate owners to rationalize farming operations by burning the cane fields prior to cutting (a technique introduced in 1967 to permit the cutting to proceed at a faster pace) and by the introduction of mechanical loaders. This process was aggravated by sharply falling sugar prices and a general decline in sugar output after 1965. Between 1960 and 1970, the number of sugar workers employed in the harvest season declined by 9,000.

In spite of the general decline in sugar production after 1965, sugar continued to play a central role in the Jamaican economy. In a 1978 report, the World Bank summarized the situation as follows:

> Despite its most recent decline, sugar is still vital to the Jamaican economy and social fabric: its cultivation represents the biggest area under a single crop (30% of "land in farms"): it is still the most valuable crop and it produces the raw material, molasses, for the production of rum and alcoholic beverages. Although the total value of sugar and sugar productions declined from 50% of total export value in 1948 to about 10% in 1976, they still provide over 50% of all agricultural export value. Sugar therefore remains the cornerstone of Jamaica's agriculture...

> The social importance of the sugar industry is illustrated by its employment directly and indirectly of about 50,000 people or 6% of the total labor

26

force and almost 20% of the labor force
in agriculture...(19)

The World Bank report also noted that:

> The skewed distribution of land, with
> the considerable underutilization of
> resources that has resulted, has been a
> major impediment to the development of
> agriculture and the prosperity of rural
> areas (20).

Fewer than one-tenth of one percent of all farms
controlled over half of the total agricultural acreage
in Jamaica, while more than three-quarters of the
farms covered only 15 percent of total acreage (20).

By the early 1970's, the failure to create a
viable, diversified agricultural sector providing
sufficient access to land and employment opportunities
for the rural population had led to widespread migration into the Kingston metropolitan area, which in
1972 housed about 30 percent of the total population
and 38 percent of Jamaica's labor force.

Superficially it would appear that Jamaica was
making great strides through the industrialization
program embarked upon in the 1960's. The economy grew
at an annual rate of about 6.5 percent. The economic
base was broadened; bauxite, alumina and tourism
became major sources of foreign exchange, with sugar
and sugar products declining in relative importance.
Many products which had been previously imported, such
as clothes, shoes, cosmetics and building materials
were now also produced in Jamaica. Industrialization
by invitation failed, however, to decrease Jamaican
dependence on foreign economic interests. In fact, it
aggravated it. In addition to being largely foreign
owned, much of the new manufacturing industry used
imported raw materials, as well as equipment and spare
parts, creating an increasing drain on available
foreign exchange funds. It also transformed Jamaica
into a major consumer of oil, all of which had to be
imported, adding further strains on foreign exchange
reserves. Profits from foreign-owned enterprises
continued to be repatriated to Europe and increasingly
to the United States. Income inequalities within the
country were extremely wide, and were becoming increasingly pronounced, acording to Carl Stone:

27

As Jamaica has diversified its economy from a simple plantation trading economy to a more complex economic system which has added modern services and manufacturing industries to that still surviving colonial economy, the distribution of income has become less evenly spread (22).

Stone also concludes that some 70 percent of the Jamaican population lives in poverty, i.e., they have incomes "representing purchasing power below the level necessary to sustain a reasonable standard of balanced nutrition, adequate clothing, satisfactory housing and child care and discretionary income for minimal leisure" (23).

The Puerto Rican "Bootstrap" style development of the Jamaican economy failed to create employment on the scale necessary to absorb the steadily mushrooming displaced and impoverished rural population. (In Puerto Rico the program has also proved incapable of sustaining high employment.) The newly added manufacturing industry was highly capital-intensive. The firms arriving under the industrialization program in the 1960's generated only some 15,000 jobs, while the labor force increased by over 100,000. The bauxite, and later alumina, industry added some 9,700 jobs. In the meantime, unemployment soared from 12 percent in 1962 to 24 percent in 1972, in spite of massive migration out of the country. Between 1950 and 1968, 270,000 Jamaicans emigrated, mainly to Great Britain, the United States and Canada. Tens of thousands more entered these countries illegally. A large mass remained trapped in Jamaica's urban slums, barely surviving on occasional wage labor, such as shoe shining, finding parking spaces, dock work, higglering (i.e. the selling of small quantities of goods), and illegal activities such as prostitution, theft and ganja (marijuana) trade. These were the 'sufferers', the urban poor, who were too poor to get out.

Three hundred years of British colonial rule and a decade of neocolonial capitalist development had by the early 1970's produced extreme income inequalities, widespread rural and urban poverty, underemployment and unemployment, deepseated dependence on external capital and large-scale migration overseas. Those left behind were yearning to "go foreign", especially

28

to the United States, in the belief that if one could only get there, one's problems would be magically solved.

The 1972 elections represented a popular indictment of the JLP government's development policy of the 1960's, in the sweeping victory of the PNP, now led by Norman Manley's son, Michael. The PNP under Michael Manley's leadership was moving again ideologically toward the left and was attracting the support of the more educated and ideologically radical workers, owners of small- or middle-sized farms and of the increasing numbers of urban poor. Although the party leadership and representation in Parliament was disproportionately in the hands of the upper and lower middle class, especially lawyers, doctors, administrators, technicians, ministers and teachers (24), the party also had the support of some sectors of the elite. The most influential of the so-called 21 families, the Matalon family, has personal ties to Michael Manley. One of its members served in the PNP cabinet, and the family was also represented in a variety of government agencies such as the Development Corporation, National Development Agency, and the Jamaica Bauxite Institute, as well as the government-owned National Hotel Properties Company (25). On the whole, though, key positions in the government bureaucracy were held by moderate or conservative party members of upper-middle-class professional status. The two main exceptions were D. K. Duncan and Hugh Small, the two most left-leaning PNP Executive Council members, who headed the Ministry of Mobilization and the Ministry of Finance, respectively, but only for a relatively short period.

After the 1972 elections the PNP moved rapidly to enact a variety of programs aimed at improving the lot of the urban and rural poor: for example, free adult, secondary and college education, land redistribution and a network of rural health clinics. In 1974, the goal of instituting democratic socialism was openly proclaimed, which was to include state control over strategic sectors of the economy, worker participation in or control of business management and a more equitable distribution of land and wealth. A national minimum-wage law was introduced, and a year later a law mandating equal pay for equal work was passed. A new property tax was introduced. In 1974, the government also moved to impose a levy on bauxite, increas-

29

ing revenues for Jamaica sevenfold. Furthermore, the government acquired 51 percent of the mining operations, 75 percent of the local telephone company, the Kingston area bus company, Barclay's Bank, and about 30 percent of resort hotel capacity in 1974 and 1975. In addition the Manley regime initiated the establishment of the National Housing Trust, a public fund for housing construction, the State Trading Corporation to import basic food, clothing and building materials, and the National Sugar Company to operate sugar factories acquired by the government. Manley led the effort to organize the International Bauxite Association, a cartel modeled after OPEC. Ties with Cuba were established and Manley became a vocal proponent of the New International Economic Order and a defender of national liberation movements such as MPLA in Angola and FRELIMO in Mozambique.

A number of the above reforms soon met with intense opposition primarily from the local business class and the wealthy who saw the new property tax, free public education, minimum wage laws and worker participation in management as a threat to their interests. The JLP-led opposition expressed increasingly virulent anti-communist sentiments (26). The transnational corporations and the United States government also perceived Manley's policies as contrary to their interests and retaliated by putting economic and ideological pressure on the regime. Within the PNP, antagonisms between the left and the conservatives erupted over such issues as popular participation in government and industrial management and the relationship to the International Monetary Fund. At the same time the government bureaucrats, so crucially important for the implementation of new policies, were putting up road blocks whenever they felt their own positions were in jeopardy.

It was in this political and economic climate that the effort to turn over to the sugar workers the three largest sugar estates -- Frome, Monymusk and Bernard Lodge -- was launched.

1. The word <u>Maroon</u> was first used by the Spanish to describe cattle that had gone wild. Later it referred to escaped Indian, and subsequently African, slaves.

2. Michael Craton, <u>Sinews of Empire. A short History of British Slavery</u>. (Anchor Books, 1974), p. 46.

3. Franklin Knight, <u>The Caribbean. The Genesis of a Fragmented Nationalism</u> (Oxford University Press, 1978), p. 238.

4. Craton, <u>op.cit.</u>, pp. 119-139.

5. Adam Smith, <u>Wealth of Nations</u>, quoted in Eric Williams, <u>Capitalism and Slavery</u>, (Capricorn Books, 1966), p. 53.

6. Williams, <u>ibid.</u>, pp. 51-84.

7. Craton, <u>op.cit.</u>, p. 205.

8. <u>Ibid.</u>, pp. 208-209.

9. <u>Ibid.</u>, p. 192.

10. Orlando Patterson, <u>The Sociology of Slavery</u>. (MacGibbon and Kee, 1967), p. 72.

11. Sir Hans Sloane, <u>Natural History of Jamaica</u>. Quoted in Patterson, <u>ibid.</u>, pp. 82-83.

12. Patterson, <u>ibid.</u>, p. 92.

13. Craton, <u>op.cit.</u>, p. 307.

14. <u>Ibid.</u>, p. 304.

15. Peter Phillips, "Jamaican Elites: 1938 to Present." in Carl Stone and Aggrey Brown, eds., <u>Essays on Power and Change in Jamaica</u>. (Jamaica Publ. House, 1977), p. 5.

16. <u>Economic Evaluation of the Jamaican Special Employment Program</u>. (Center for Economic Studies, Palo Alto, 1977), p. 15.

17. Carl Feuer, Jamaica and Sugar Worker Coopera-
    tives: The Politics of Reform. (Ph.D. Diss.
    Cornell University, 1983), table 3.1, p. 58.

18. Carl Feuer estimated that sugar worker incomes
    declined by as much as 40% between 1963 and 1972,
    based on Monymusk data. Ibid, p. 85.

19. The World Bank, Staff Appraisal Report. Sugar
    Rehabilitation Project. Jamaica. January 19,
    1978, p. 9.

20. Ibid., p. 2.

21. Land Distribution in Jamaica: (late 1970's)

Farm Size	Number of Farms	Percent of Agricultural Acreage
500 acres +	630	42
100-500 acres	800	13
50-100 acres	1,815	5
25-50 acres	1,755	3
5-25 acres	37,000	22
5 acres -	150,000	15
TOTAL	192,000	100

Source: Ibid., p. 2.

22. Carl Stone, Democracy and Clientelism in Jamaica.
    (Transaction Books, 1980), p. 53.

23. Ibid., pp. 51-52, 54.

24. In the 1976 parliamentary elections 85 percent of
    the PNP candidates were of the middle class, 10
    percent were planters or merchants, only 5
    percent were small farmers and 0 percent of
    working-class status. Rank and file party
    activists, however, were drawn primarily from
    among the unemployed, small peasantry and lower
    working class. Stone, ibid., pp. 133-34.

25. Ibid., p. 215.

26. The JLP in the 1970's was becoming increasingly dominated by capitalist interests and business-related professionals, with mass support coming especially from rural workers and the petty traders, or higglers.

CHAPTER II

MOBILIZATION

> During 1973 the Social Action Centre
> began to plant some seeds in the rich
> fields of Monymusk. The seed was the
> mere idea of worker control of these
> vast estate lands by means of coopera-
> tives, and the fields were the deeply-
> felt longings of the sugar workers, who
> had labored on these lands for genera-
> tions and had never been allowed to
> possess an acre. (Joe Owens)

The movement to establish workers' control on
three of the largest sugar estates was a continuation
of the efforts by Jamaican sugar workers to free
themselves from centuries of oppression. Their
earlier struggles culminated in the organization of
trade unions such as the BITU, the TUC and later the
NWU, and led the sugar workers to adopt the union
ideology of an adversary relationship between workers
and management. The notion of cooperatives was new to
them; it had to be introduced by a source outside the
unions. That source was a small group of activists
from the Jesuit-founded Social Action Centre (SAC).

Organizers from SAC planted the seed of cooperative ideology among the sugar workers, mobilized them
and nourished the cooperatives during their seedling
stages. The sugar workers and their leaders gave life
and form to the cooperative idea, and their dedication
and hard work enabled the young cooperatives to take
root and grow. Meanwhile, as we shall see below,
officials from the Ministry of Agriculture, the
government-owned Frome Monymusk Land Company and the
farm staff that worked under them stunted that growth
by shaping the implementation of the cooperatives in
such a way as to preserve their own influence and
limit the workers' gains.

A Favorable Climate

The birth of the cooperatives resulted from
a confluence of several forces that provided the
necessary conditions for their development. The
deterioration of the plantation system and the dismal
prospects of earning profits from growing sugar cane

had made the transnational corporate owners -- Tate & Lyle and the United Fruit Co. -- eager to divest themselves of the three estates. WISCO, the Tate & Lyle subsidiary, had lost $J5.5 million on its operations at Frome and Monymusk between 1967 and 1970 alone (1). The negotiations and the sale of the estates to the government took place while the JLP was still in power. The three large estates were bought for about $J10 million, with the understanding that the money would be recouped by resale of the farms to middle and wealthy Jamaican cane farmers. The purchase was probably inspired at least in part by nationalism and by the JLP government's desire to help its own supporters, adding to the land held by Jamaican cane farmers and providing continuing employment for sugar workers (2).

The accession to power by the People's National Party in 1972 provided the necessary change in the political atmosphere which facilitated the mobilization of the sugar workers into cooperatives. The new Prime Minister, Michael Manley, reversed the decision of the previous government to sell the estates in large parcels to private owners and instead began considering alternative ways of managing sugar cane production. Although he was not prepared to alter the predominance of the managerial class, Manley hoped to inaugurate a new era for the working people of Jamaica. He envisioned a modification of the capitalist social order, not its abolition, through workers' participation rather than workers' control (3). Manley was undoubtedly interested in trying to win the support of the 50,000 sugar workers on the island, most of whom had been strong supporters of the JLP and members of the JLP-affiliated BITU.

A 1972 PNP Cabinet paper stated that cooperatives (not specifically described at this time) would be given priority in the development of the three government-owned estates. In September 1972, Manley said, "I am determined that a way has got to be found to create a method for workers to share in the ownership. We, for instance, have very big plans for the sugar lands we own at Frome, Monymusk and Bernard Lodge."

The government's early proposals for the transformation of the three estates called for individual land leases, with 25-30 individuals or families each leasing 30-40 acre plots grouped into 1000 acre blocks, sharing cooperative services. These plans would have benefited only a minority of the previously employed sugar workers, who in all likelihood would have been primarily supervisors and other more literate persons in the upper stratum of the workforce. The bureaucracy would "naturally" find them easier to deal with than the semi-literate majority. Also, there was to be a long phasing-in process over several years, with centralized management and administrative control of cooperative services by the government rather than by the workers themselves (4). The detailed planning was delegated to the Frome Monymusk Land company, the caretaker organization set up by the previous government to administer the estates until sold to private farmers, because this organization included officials already involved in managing the sugar estates. Most of the executives and staff employees of the Land Company were carried over from their previous employment with the transnational sugar companies. The government's intention was for the Land Company technocrats (including Winston Higgins, who had some previous experience with cooperatives in other countries and who was appointed Cooperative Development Officer) to plan cooperatives on behalf of the sugar workers but without their active participation in the process.

Planting the Seeds

Vague as they were, the government's statements about transforming the three sugar estates into some kind of cooperatives provided a green light for grass roots organizing by Social Action Centre members and sugar worker leaders. The Centre grew out of the determination of several Jesuit priests to bring about social justice through the transformation of Jamaican society, highly polarized between a small wealthy elite and the poverty-stricken masses.

SAC originated during the 1930's, and its early work was concentrated mainly on the development of credit unions. Its initial contact with the workers on the estates came during the early 1970's when SAC members tried unsuccessfully to organize housing cooperatives. By 1972, the group was searching for a new project. Manley's decision to transform some of the government-held sugar lands into cooperatives provided SAC the opportunity it had been seeking. According to one of its members:

36

The Social Action Centre saw the Government's policy for the sugar lands as an opportunity, an opening, for moving the country in a socialist direction, provided certain conditions of extensiveness, education and struggle were met. Unashamedly, the motivation was political (5).

Much of the dynamic energy that went into the early organizing effort was supplied by Joseph Owens, a young Jesuit priest from the United States who joined SAC in 1972. Owens had been involved in SAC's attempt to organize cooperative housing at Monymusk. At Owen's suggestion, SAC agreed to try organizing cooperative cane farms on the large estates. Owens made a number of trips to Monymusk and by the middle of 1972 he moved from the capital, Kingston, to live amongst the workers in one of the many settlements adjacent to the sugar estate. After a year of talking and listening to the workers, Owens, with the help of receptive sugar workers, began organizing local committees of those interested in cooperatives.

By July 1973, a dozen committees had been formed, stretching from one end of the 30,000 acre Monymusk estate to the other. Eventually they were to form the backbone of the Sugar Workers' Cooperative Council (SWCC), a mass membership organization that united all those sugar workers who were interested in transforming the cane farms into cooperatives. The committees had a fluctuating membership of perhaps 5 to 15 and at that time included small farmers as well as sugar workers.

The organization spread through Horace Levy, who joined SAC in 1973, and Neville Wong to Frome and Bernard Lodge, respectively. The workers at Bernard Lodge, being close to Kingston, were the most literate and highly conscious group of any on the three government-held estates. They were most receptive to the idea of workers control and developed their own organization without relying as heavily on SAC as the workers at the other two estates.

The SAC members did not bring with them any clear-cut blueprint for cooperatives. At first, Owens, Levy and the others at the Centre had in mind marketing and purchasing cooperatives similar to those

planned by the government, based on individual leaseholds with cooperative use of tractors and cooperative
purchasing. Only later, as they realized the shortcomings of plans that would provide employment mainly
for the well-to-do fraction of the sugar workers, did
their emphasis change to favor collectively-run
producers' cooperatives. In the latter, production as
well as service is collective; such cooperatives are
worker-controlled with an elected governing board that
appoints and discharges managers, while final authority resides in the membership.

The first reaction of many sugar workers to the
SAC organizers and to the cooperative idea was one of
suspicion and skepticism. They were used to the empty
promises of the politicians whose rhetoric hardly ever
led to measureable improvements in the workers' lives
(6). Matthias Brown, who later was to become an SWCC
organizer himself, recalls:

> (SAC organizer Horace) Levy had a
> meeting in the square and I was there
> listening to him telling the people
> that the estate land can be turned over
> to the people if they form themselves
> in a cooperative. I was very skeptical
> not only of this plan but of the man
> himself. It was strange to me to find
> a person coming to tell me that we can
> own the land. In fact at the meetings
> there in the early stages I was even
> heckling (him) (7).

Cleaveland Dobson, a spade man and cane cutter from
Frome, tells of his first impressions of the SAC
organizers:

> They mentioned that they were not sent
> by any government, neither by a union
> nor committed to any church. We were
> looking that in a situation like this
> in a country like this, they couldn't
> just come by themselves.

In spite of their initial scepticism, small
groups of workers were organized first in the communities surrounding the estates and later directly on the
farms. The workers were ready for any change that
promised to improve their conditions. Many of those

38

who joined the cooperative committees were motivated by a deep-seated anger and hatred of the plantation system:

> They knew the estate system was rotten to the core, that whole hierarchical system and the favoritism and the victimization that went on. They really believed in themselves, that they could do better themselves. The workers realized that they were just peons and they were extremely angry about that. (Joe Owens)

The several cooperative committees that had been formed at Monymusk joined together to form the Monymusk Workers Cooperative Cane Farming Association (8). The Monymusk and Frome committees in turn were linked in October 1973, when two bus loads of Monymusk activists came to Frome to found the Sugar Workers' Cooperative Council (SWCC). Concurrently between 10 and 20 Monymusk workers were traveling regularly to Bernard Lodge to help with cooperative organizing there (9). By the end of 1973, the SWCC had over 600 members in a score of local councils that met regularly to discuss the proposals for establishing cooperatives and to insure that the workers would take part in any distribution of the estate lands.

Preparing the Ground

With grant funds obtained for the purpose by SAC from the Inter-American Foundation (10), the SWCC employed about two dozen sugar workers and a few interested "outsiders", such as progressive university students, as paid co-op organizers on the three estates (11). These SAC organizers formed an important part of the leadership of the SWCC. The leaders dedicated their time and energy to the vision of farms owned and controlled by the sugar workers. Undoubtedly, some also perceived in the planned cooperatives an opportunity for upward social mobility and personal advancement that they could not otherwise have found within rigidly stratified estates. The organizers were recruited from among the more literate sugar workers, because they would be able to cope with written educational materials, and because many of them represented "opinion leaders" to whom the less literate workers often looked for advice. For the same reasons many of them had already been promoted to supervisory positions on their farms. All of them were men. They were drawn from among sympathizers of both major political parties.

SAC provided free training for sugar workers and the SWCC leaders, usually in the form of weekend seminars for 40-50 persons, including 2 or 3 from each farm on the three estates. The training included courses in cooperative principles, business management, running committee meetings, strategy in dealing with staff, and communicating with other workers. Those who attended the seminars in turn reached out to their fellow workers, discussing with them the shortcomings of the existing plantation system and the benefits of replacing it with cooperatives. For two years, the organizers held meetings on the estates where they would discuss co-op ideas and principles within small groups that met every other week; there were about seven or eight such groups on each estate. The organizers used monthly bulletins, in spite of the high level of member illiteracy, and held literacy classes using SAC-prepared materials that had a heavy co-op and historical content. At Monymusk, 100-200 workers out of a workforce of some 2000 used to gather once a month on Sundays to listen to the organizers discuss the progress of the movement. The message the SWCC leaders brought to the workers was that they were capable of running their own business and that they as producers should be entitled to a share of the profits. Also, that they should work together towards independence from the government and the unions in order to get real control of the farms. The ultimate objective, the SAC and SWCC organizers thought, should be to work toward the establishment of cooperatives throughout the sugar industry, including the factories, and throughout the rest of the Jamaican economy as well.

The First Seeds Sprout

The grass roots organizing campaign of the SWCC helped convince the government to hasten the implementation of its own plans.

In June 1973, over a year after Father Owens' arrival at Monymusk, the SWCC invited Winston Higgins, the Frome Monymusk Land Company's Cooperative Development Officer, to address a meeting at Monymusk.

Higgins told the workers that the government was planning for cooperatives and that he himself hoped that three pilot cooperatives would be functioning by the end of the year. In October 1973, the leaders of the SWCC and their advisors from the Social Action Centre met with the Minister of Agriculture, Keble Munn, who informed them that three pilot cooperatives were about to be established. At the same time, the SWCC submitted a petition to Prime Minister Manley urging expeditious action. Manley congratulated the SWCC on forming an organization for cooperative development on the three estates, but did not share any specific plans with them. In January 1974, Manley addressed a meeting in Lionel Town where he said he could not rest satisfied until he saw the Frome Monymusk Land Company lands farmed cooperatively by the workers employed on those estates. It was to take further prodding by the workers' leaders before these words were turned into reality.

The government's decision to move ahead with the cooperatives resulted from the pressure exerted by the SWCC, now a mass organization of hundreds of members, and from the leftward movement of the PNP at that time. The latter was symbolized by Prime Minister Manley's public pronouncement in 1974 that the party was committed to democratic socialism. Early that year the PNP government finally named a new Managing Director for the Land Company and replaced its con-servative Board of Directors with more liberal ap-pointees, including three workers, one of whom was Stanford Phillips, the Chairman of the Monymusk SWCC. But at the same time the PNP government reacted ambivalently to the drive by SAC and the SWCC to mobilize the sugar workers, partly because it involved the independent organizing of a large group of workers outside of the existing union/party structures. The left wing of the PNP supported the mobilization effort, while officials of the Ministry of Agricul-ture, the Cooperative Department, and the Frome Monymusk Land Company were unhappy about the SWCC organizing campaign. The strategy of forming an independent organization was successful, however, in influencing the government to take action on the cooperative idea. It was only after the SWCC became active as a mass organization that the government finally moved to implement the decision to begin the three pilot co-ops, and at the same time adopted a more radical vision of the proposed cooperatives.

In late 1973, the SAC activists, SWCC leaders, the government and the Land Company were still thinking in terms of purchasing or marketing cooperatives based on small individual leaseholds. When it became apparent that such a plan would benefit only a small fraction of the sugar workers, the SWCC and SAC began to consider the idea of collectively-owned producers' cooperatives that would embrace all the workers who were at that time employed on the three estates. In early 1974, two of the new board members of the Land Company, Carl Stone and Richard Fletcher (12), helped persuade the government to adopt the vision of collectively instead of individually leased land.

Another bone of contention was the question of co-op farm size. SWCC and SAC preferred moderate-sized farms of a few hundred acres each that would be operated by small teams of workers. They believed that a smaller size would make it easier for the members to closely identify themselves with their business and to exert more direct control over farm affairs. The government favored the retention of the pre-existing 2000 acre farms thinking that this would make the change-over easier by causing only minimal alterations in cane production. Looking back on those days, former SAC member Joe Owens commented:

> We resisted at the onset the idea of taking the existing farms and making them into cooperatives, because they just seemed too unwieldy. They seemed more designed for the same type of corporate management which they had known for the previous 20 or more years. But the government was pretty insistent on doing it that way. They thought that somehow these were pre-existing units and the workforce was already in place and to go ahead with that seemed the wisest thing. We didn't have enough resources ourselves to develop a whole other plan, so we just went along and concentrated our educational efforts accordingly.

On the other hand, as a result of continuous agitation by the SWCC, the government dropped its insistence on centralized government administration of the co-ops, and agreed at least in theory to a significant degree of sugar workers' control of the farms.

After a years' organizing effort, the SWCC had generated enough publicity and pressure for the government to hasten its plans for the pilot co-ops. Three farms of about 2000 acres each were chosen as pilot projects: Barham at Frome, Morelands at Monymusk, and Great Salt Pond at Bernard Lodge. What finally moved the government to begin the actual implementation of the pilot co-ops was a demonstration in Kingston organized by some of the Frome workers. About 25-30 activist SWCC members from the Barham and Georges Plain farms at Frome came to Kingston. SAC member Levy, who accompanied them, describes the scene:

> We gathered in the churchyard at the Holy Cross Church near Half Way Tree (A major Kingston intersection). We went and paraded outside the Jamaica Broadcasting Corporation, demanding that the cooperatives start. We did go to the Prime Minister's office. We didn't get in; we stayed outside, but it got into the papers, it came over the air.

Prime Minister Manley requested an explanation from Desmond Leakey, Parliamentary Secretary for Agriculture and also the Chairman of the Frome Monymusk Land Company. Within several weeks of the demonstration a committee was established within the Land Company to finalize plans for the pilot cooperatives and to prepare guidelines for their operation. According to these plans the Land Company was to provide managerial services and such technical services as tractor work and irrigation under contract to the pilot farms. Details were to be worked out in negotiations between the Land Company and workers' representatives. Elections were held on the three farms, in which almost all of the workers participated; most of the workers from the previous cooperative organizing committees were chosen to the eleven member farm Managing Committees.

Shortly before Christmas 1974, workers' leaders from Barham, Salt Pond and Morelands signed long-term lease contracts giving their 500 members control over 6000 acres in cane lands. The pilot farms were still

43

integrated into their respective estates, but were to operate as cooperatives. Finally in January 1975, the three pilot co-ops began their work of cultivating and harvesting cane under worker control. This was indeed a historical occasion for Jamaican sugar workers; descendants of slaves and former workers for the giant transnational corporations won title to some of the best agricultural land in the country, together with the right to determine farm policies and the right to decide how profits would be spent. The establishment of the pilot co-ops necessitated a shift in formal power between the workers and staff. No longer did the managers, mostly inherited from the former owners, rule unchallenged, responsible only to their supervisors in the estate hierarchy. Now at least in theory the eleven workers elected to the Managing Committee of each farm set policies which would have to be carried out by their hired managers. As SAC organizer Owens points out,

> For the first time in four centuries sugar workers realize that they are in control of their own land, their own business, their own lives. All material benefits aside, this is revolutionary.

In practice, the weight of tradition and the carryover of former managers made the implementation of workers' control far from easy.

The Winds of Conflict

Even as the pilot cooperatives were being established, the organizers redoubled their efforts to create cooperatives on the remaining 20 farms on the three estates. By the beginning of 1975 cooperative organizing committees had been established on all the farms. This mobilization drive encountered strong opposition, however. Some came from JLP supporters and from the JLP-affiliated BITU which nominally represented about 70 percent of the sugar workers, though there was resistance from the rival PNP-affiliated NWU as well.

The JLP politicians and activists spoke out against the cooperatives because they continued to favor private enterprise and foreign investment, and because the cooperatives meant a reversal of that party's original plan to sell off the sugar estates in large parcels to private owners. The unions, which formed an important part of the political power base of the parties they were allied with, were afraid that under a system of worker ownership they would lose some 5000 members as well as their union dues. The unions used such influence as they had at the governmental level as well as among their local representatives on the farms to work against the formation of the co-ops and later to oppose them once they had begun. The SWCC organizers were able to sign up the sugar workers in spite of their union membership, however, because the unions had become relatively inactive on the three estates and the workers did not perceive them as doing much on their behalf. The unions' role was limited to periodic collective bargaining for wage rates at the national level.

Major opposition to the cooperatives also came from the managers and other staff at the farm and estate levels who had been employed by the transnational corporations and who continued in their positions after the government acquired the estates. The staff perceived the cooperatives as a potential threat to their prerogatives, which included the power to grant or withhold work for the sugar workers, to spend money as they saw fit, and to promote their favorites to supervisory positions. The staff saw their income and their very jobs threatened by the co-ops; they feared that the implementation of workers' control might lead to pressure to channel farm income away from the employees and toward the sugar workers, and to economy measures that could result in reducing the total number of staff. Some staff used their influence with the sugar workers (who through years of subservience had become used to heeding the managers' suggestions) to persuade them not to join the SWCC. A few even spread rumors about the Social Action Centre. Sometimes SAC was said to be Communist and sometimes its members were accused of working for the American CIA.

The farm managers, or bushas, who had been used to running the farms as they liked and were only loosely supervised by the estate executives, felt especially threatened by the proposed co-ops. Some of them used every means at their disposal, including the assignment and withholding of work, to make the task of the organizers more difficult. The SWCC committees

that had been established on the farms and estates
were initially barred from meeting at their work-
places. The bushas also took reprisals against those
who went to Kingston to attend inter-estate worker
meetings. Organizer Matthias Brown recounts that,
after returning from such a meeting:

> My boss would tell me that I couldn't
> work on a Saturday or a Sunday, and
> those days were premium days when you
> would earn most money. So I would have
> to be content with three days or four
> days per week pay and that time I was
> getting J$1.85 per day.

The bushas realized that for the proposed cooperatives to succeed, the workers would have to increase
their literacy, and their knowledge about cooperative
principles and about cane farming as a business. So
they refused to give workers time off to attend
classes offered by the organizers, maintaining that
this detracted from production (13).

Another source of resistance to the grass-roots
cooperative movement came from within the government
itself. The government bureaucrats favored cooperatives only if they could be contained and controlled
by them. They were suspicious of any independent
organizing efforts that were not sponsored by the
Cooperative Department or the government-owned Frome
Monymusk Land Company. The Land Company officials
tried to deflect the SWCC organizing campaign by
setting up its own workers' committees on each farm
parallel to the SWCC committees. These parallel
committees, appointed by Land Company officials and
each including two staff representatives, never
actually began functioning, but the Land Company's
attempt to create such committees reflected its
top-down mentality and distrust of workers control
(14).

Although left-wing PNP leaders such as Hugh Small
and D. K. Duncan continued to support the mobilization
drive, the center and right-wing factions within the
ruling party saw the grass roots organizing by the
SWCC and its allies in the Social Action Centre as
potentially endangering government control of the
supply of sugar cane needed to keep the factories
running. The Social Action Centre was viewed by both

government as well as the JLP-led opposition as a threat to the existing parties and unions to the extent that it succeeded in building a new organization among the sugar workers not directly tied to either of the major unions or the political parties with which each was allied. The ambivalence of the government toward the grass-roots mobilization drive by SWCC and SAC was a reflection of a political party divided between right- and left-wing factions with Prime Minister Manley perched in the middle. One of the most trusted of Manley's advisors on the sugar industry, Richard Fletcher, characterized SAC as "well meaning but romantic and irresponsible (15)." At the same time as Prime Minister Manley was making statements in support of the cooperatives, officials in the Cooperative Department and the Land Company were resisting the organizing efforts of the SWCC.

Almost as soon as the three pilot farms began operation, two education drives were mounted: the official program of the Land Company and the Cooperative Department coordinated by Cedric McCulloch, and the unofficial efforts of SAC and the SWCC worker committees. The Cooperative Department's work was limited by the fact that it had only a small number of education staff based on the three pilot co-ops and by the fact that its personnel lacked the kind of rapport that the SWCC field organizers had developed with the other sugar workers. The SWCC at this time concentrated its efforts on the other 20 farms which were not yet cooperatives, so the two education programs could have been complementary. Considerable animosity developed, however, between the two education groups, reflecting divergent philosophies of what the cooperatives were all about. McCulloch and Land Company officials gave lip service to workers' participation while supporting the kind of cooperative structure that would continue the dominance of the managers. Their vision was one of a "company cooperative" similar to a company union:

> In the company cooperative the (hold-over) staff would have selected in effect the workers' representatives. The staff would have been members and would have dominated. We did not in fact exclude the staff from membership. But our position was that if the staff were to be members they would have to

47

be members on the same footing as the
workers. (SAC organizer Horace Levy)

The vision of cooperatives run from the top down was
probably shared by Prime Minister Manley himself. In
at least one public statement he declared that staff
were workers, with the implication that control of the
farms by the staff was all right since they, too, were
workers.

Another difference between the Cooperative
Department and the SWCC organizers was over the kind
of leases to be granted to the remaining 20 estate
farms when they became cooperatives. The pilot co-ops
had received individual leases directly from the
government, and the Cooperative Department favored
this for any additional farms that were to be convert-
ed to cooperatives. The SWCC argued that when more
co-ops were added there should be a two-tier structure
in which all the cooperative farms on any given estate
would belong to a secondary-level cooperative. Under
such an arrangement, leases would be awarded to three
estate cooperatives which in turn would sublease the
land to individual farm co-ops. The SWCC favored
estate leases because its leaders felt this arrangement would keep the fledgling workers' movement
unified and increase worker solidarity through a
structure that emphasized their interdependence. The
Cooperative Department favored autonomous farms with
individually held leases, perhaps perceiving in such
an arrangement a better opportunity for its officials
to influence the farms.

The conflict between the rival education programs
escalated. Cedric McCulloch promoted the idea of
individual leases and the "company cooperative" model
through his contact with individual sugar workers on a
number of the farms and through his alliance with the
leadership of Monymusk Tractor and Transport (a division of the government-owned Monymusk estate responsible for providing plowing and hauling services to
each of the farms). McCulloch and some of the staff
joined in a propaganda campaign against the Social
Action Centre and the SWCC leaders that threatened to
split the cooperative movement into two factions. SAC
organizer Joe Owens recounts the struggle over the
leases:

I really feel that it was McCulloch who
was orchestrating the opposition (to
SAC in general and to estate leases in
particular). It reached such a serious
pitch that at one point Tractor and
Transport sent a whole crowd of workers
--it must have been a hundred of them--
to Kingston to talk to the Minister of
Agriculture (about awarding leases to
individual farms). They made a very
threatening pass by the Social Action
Centre, waving their fists and shout-
ing. It was just crazy. It wasn't
just McCulloch and his crowd. There
were also a lot of staff people on the
estate who seized every opportunity to
disrupt worker harmony and unity.

The lease controversy was finally resolved by a
compromise that allowed several farms (in addition to
the three pilot co-ops) to choose individual leases,
with the bulk of the land leased to the three estate
cooperatives that were to be formed. The SWCC organizers felt they had won this battle, and they continued to spread the cooperative message to the sugar
workers on all three estates.

Two circumstances helped the organizers win over
many sugar workers to the cooperative idea. Excep-
tionally high world sugar prices during 1974 enabled
the three pilot co-ops to show a profit during their
first year and made the other workers feel that if
they joined the cooperatives they, too, would share
such profits. Also, the government had promised a
lump-sum payment of severance money, amounting in many
cases to several thousand dollars, to any who joined
the cooperatives. The possibility of obtaining a
large sum of money from the severance payments swayed
many workers into joining the SWCC even though they
understood little about cooperative principles.

Worker unity was impeded by the fight over the
leases, however. For a time, three farms at Monymusk
and the Tractor and Transport unit there opposed the
SWCC and refused to join the proposed estate cooperative. The atmosphere of recrimination and conflict
among the sugar workers that resulted from arguments
about the form of the lease was an inauspicious

49

beginning for the remaining cooperatives that were soon to be formed.

Expanding the Fields

By mid-1975, the SWCC organizing campaign had succeeded in signing up some 2000 of the 5000 workers at Frome, Monymusk and Bernard Lodge to join cooperatives. The success of this drive persuaded the government to speed up the transformation of most of the farms on the three estates into cooperatives, despite its own plans for a slow transition. At first, the government had planned to add a few farms per year as co-ops so that all the farms on the three estates would become cooperatives over a six- or seven-year period.

Within the Social Action Centre there was some debate over how quickly to convert the three estates to cooperatives. Owens was uneasy about moving too fast without establishing a sound core of worker leaders who were adequately trained and grounded in experience. He believed that only very capable leaders could actually oversee the management of farms that grossed over a million Jamaican dollars each, and could stand their ground in any controversy with the staff members who had so much more education then they. Levy was more inclined to push ahead. His argument that the pace of converting the remaining farms to cooperatives should maximize the possibility of workers' control prevailed. Levy explains:

> It was a question whether the workers were to control (cane production) or not. If the workers were to control, then they had to control at every level, at farm, estate and inter-estate levels. This was the key, the critical factor. No use giving them the land, but not passing over to them the services and the finance. So it wasn't from our perspective a quantitative thing, that we wanted this number of farms. We wanted a certain qualitative change, full worker control. Now if the workers were to control it did have a quantitative aspect, that the majority of the farms had to go (cooperative).

50

The Social Action Centre members felt that because of the workers' previous lack of training, one year was too short a time to complete all the preparatory work that would have enabled the worker committees to become fully capable of managing the farms. Further, data provided by the Land Company made SAC aware that some of the farms would not be economically viable if they continued producing cane as in the past, because the yield from so many of the cane fields was too low. Problems with irrigation made much of the land at Monymusk marginal at best, for example. Yet, the SAC members felt that if the SWCC did not take advantage of the momentum generated by its rapidly increased membership and by the favorable political climate, the opposition to the cooperatives would succeed in either stifling or co-opting the cooperative movement. Even Joe Owens agreed that:

> The only way that we could reach anything like real worker control was by pushing ahead at a breakneck speed and getting as many co-ops through at one time as possible. And by arranging it so that workers found themselves in positions of control such that nobody was going to be able to argue very much against them.

Throughout 1975, the SWCC continued its organizing at an accelerated pace. A flurry of demonstrations, mass meetings and petitions convinced the government to meet with SWCC leaders to discuss transformation of the rest of the farms to cooperatives. Prime Minister Manley set up a planning committee consisting of representatives from SWCC, SAC, the Frome Monymusk Land Company, the Cooperative Department, the two national unions and the estate Staff Associations to consider the transition. As a result of Manley's personal intervention to indicate he approved of moving ahead, the planning committee agreed that formation of cooperatives should proceed at the other farms provided that they met several criteria for readiness: two-thirds of the workers on each farm had to sign up for co-op membership and agree to purchase $20 shares; the members had to pass an oral quiz designed to test their knowledge of cooperative principles; they had to elect a Managing Committee; the workers and staff had to agree on a farm manager; and the farms had to be economically viable.

Following the agreement of the government and the planning committee on these criteria, the organizers redoubled their efforts. Temporarily overcoming their differences, the Cooperative Department, SWCC leaders and SAC organizers collaborated in drawing up quiz sheets and questionnaires. In preparation for the test, SWCC activists went out to the farms to review with the workers such cooperative fundamentals as the powers and responsibilities of the Managing Committees, of Committee Chairpersons, and of the general membership. Much to the surprise of everyone involved, including the organizers themselves, the workers at almost all of the farms had grasped enough of the complexities of co-op principles to pass the agreed-upon standards; well over two-thirds of the sugar workers on all three estates signed up to buy shares in the co-ops.

It is doubtful whether the criterion of economic viability was ever seriously applied, and even whether the necessary feasibility studies were available to the members of the planning committee before they made their decisions. The government, interested in maximizing its factories' cane supply, assumed the cooperatives would continue to retain considerable acreage of marginally productive land in cane, even though this would burden the co-ops with extra costs. Government officials were also aware that the Frome and Monymusk estates had a labor surplus, and that most of the Monymusk farms would probably not be viable without large investments to improve irrigation.

Discussions between the workers' leaders and the government culminated in a gathering held at the Trelawney Beach Hotel in August 1975. At this meeting, final plans were made for the formation of additional cooperatives. There it was agreed that 17 farms that had passed most of the criteria would become cooperatives, while three farms at Frome whose members had failed to pass were to be continued under the jurisdiction of the Land Company (16). A three-level structure, inclusive of the farms on all three estates, was drawn up, with the cane farms constituting the primary co-op level (see Figure 2.1). The service departments such as Tractors and Transport

FIGURE 2.1 ORGANIZATIONAL STRUCTURE OF FROME SUGAR WORKERS' COOPERATIVES
(arrows indicate lines of authority)

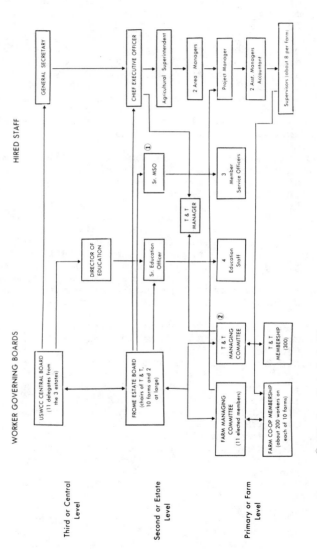

① MSO refers to Member Service Officers.

② T & T refers to Tractor and Transport. It's Managing Committee had 11 members.

53

formed their own primary cooperatives alongside the
farm co-ops. Their costs were to be collectively paid
by the cane farms. The estate or secondary level
co-ops were to supervise tractor, transport and
irrigation services for the farms and to coordinate
primary farm activities. At the third level, the
central co-op was to provide marketing, financial,
accounting, purchasing and other services for all the
estates and was to serve as a link between the cooperatives and the government bureaucracy, the Sugar
Industry Authority, and the banks. Under pressure of
an impending staff strike, the co-ops agreed to retain
the hard-to-replace technical and managerial staff who
had been working for the transnational companies and
later the Land Company.

The first phase of the movement to organize the
sugar workers concluded with the election of workers'
representatives to the farm-level Managing Committees,
the Estate Boards and the Central Board (see Figure
2.1). The farm workers were to elect eleven of their
peers to a Managing Committee, which was, at least
theoretically, to serve as the extension of their
collective power in running a farm. The organizers
made every effort to ensure maximum possible participation of the workers in these elections, and in fact
about 80 percent of the members voted. Horace Levy
described the ingenious method adopted to facilitate
balloting in spite of the low level of literacy:

> We had symbols for each nominee, and as
> people nominated somebody a symbol
> would be assigned to this person. We
> would have the nominees up on the plat-
> form, with the symbols attached to
> their chests. We would then do a
> ballot paper with the name and the
> symbol and this would be stencilled
> right then and there while further
> discussions were held. And there would
> be persons from other farms, workers
> who were literate to come and assist
> those who could not read and write, who
> at least could put a mark next to a
> symbol.

The Estate Boards included the Managing Committee
Chairpersons from each farm of the estate, and eleven
delegates from the three estates made up the Central

Board of the United Sugar Workers' Cooperative Council
(USWCC). Most of those elected to these workers'
governing committees and boards were men (17) and
about half of them were supervisors. At Frome the
majority of committee members were BITU members and
JLP supporters, while at Monymusk and Bernard Lodge
the committees had more PNP supporters. The Managing
Committees and the Estate and Central Boards chose
their own chairpersons, all of whom were men and most
of whom were former SWCC organizers. The first
Central Board members were Lloyd Vassell, Canute
Hermitt, Iseah Senior and Stanford Phillips of Monymusk; Alexander James, Matthias Brown, Charles Edwards
and Cecil Campbell of Frome; and Sidney Jones, Dudley
Hall and T. Chambers of Bernard Lodge. At the first
meeting of the Central Board in December 1975 the
board members elected Stanford Phillips as Chairman
and Iseah Senior as Secretary of the USWCC.

With the formal establishment of the USWCC, the
SWCC ceased to exist. Most of the SAC organizers and
SWCC leaders became integrated into the Managing
Committees of the USWCC, or filled the new Member
Service positions at each of the estates. The main
energies of the leaders shifted from mobilization of
the workers to the challenge of running the cane farms
as a cooperative business.

The year 1975 marked the high point of the
mobilization drive. In spite of the lingering divisions engendered by the lease controversy, the mood of
the workers' leaders was cautiously optimistic. After
all, the workers had won control over 70,000 acres of
estate land! The successful mobilization ushered in a
new era for thousands of cane workers on three of
Jamaica's largest sugar estates. This momentous
occasion was seen by some of the workers' organizers
and leaders as a first step in the implementation of
democratic socialism and of a cooperative movement
which would sweep the whole country, with workers'
control of the other sugar estates, the sugar factories, and eventually all the industries in Jamaica.
Workers Time proclaimed "Victory for Sugar Workers" in
a banner headline (see Figure 2.2). The actual
conversion of the farms to worker-controlled cane
production, however, was to be far from smooth, as the
co-op members were struggling with enormous economic
difficulties, intransigent staff and divisions amongst
themselves.

Fig. 2.2 Front Page of Workers Time, vol.1, no.1, February 1976

Victory for Sugar Workers

The beginning of the 1976 sugar crop a few short weeks ago marked one of the most important victories in the struggle by workers in Jamaica to free themselves from economic slavery.

BUSHA DAYS DONE

When the crop began at Frome New Year's Day, the workers who were burning and cutting cane were burning and cutting their own cane. They were no longer working for WISCO, for FMLCO, for "busha" or even for the government. They were working for themselves, for their brothers and sisters and for their children.

This success was achieved by the SWCC members at Frome, Monymusk and Bernard Lodge, in spite of efforts by various people to sabotage the workers' movement and turn back the struggle.

RESISTANCE

Some members of the WISCO/FMLCO staff tried to start the crop without even consulting the Managing Committees on the farms. One manager even refused to take orders from the SWCC Estate Board.

The workers did not stand for this and the SWCC Estate Boards at Frome, Monymusk and Bernard Lodge decided that no crop would start until it had been made quite clear that the Estate Boards were now in control and there was some document signifying this.

The workers also demanded an end to attempts to force on the Cooperatives those few members of the WISCO/FMLCO staff who had been rejected by workers because of their anti-SWCC attitudes.

WORKERS STAND FIRM

In making these demands workers took note of statements by the Prime Minister, when he visited the estates and addressed workers on Tuesday, December 16, that workers should make all the important decisions about the running of the estates.

The decision not to start the crop was taken Saturday night, December 27. On Monday the Parliamentary Secretary in the Ministry of Agriculture and Chairman of the Frome Monymusk Land Company, Mr. Desmond Leaky, flew to Frome and held talks with worker representatives from all three estates.

An agreement was reached at this meeting that Mr. Leaky would write a letter to each of the three SWCC Estate Co-op Boards giving the workers possession of the estate lands pending completion of the lease documents. The workers then undertook to start the crop on New Year's Day, beginning at Frome.

THE STRUGGLE CONTINUES

This battle has been won but the struggle continues. The struggle continues to free the workers in the factories, to free the workers on other estates, to free all workers in all industries in Jamaica.

1. Carl Stone, "An Appraisal of the Cooperative Process in the Jamaican Sugar Industry," _Social and Economic Studies,_ 27:1, March 1978, Table 1, p. 3.

2. According to Sugar Industry Authority Chairperson Richard Fletcher, "Their (the JLP government's) idea was, having bought this land at $200 an acre, they would sell it off in sort of 500-acre plots to farmers--most likely the overseers and senior staff members--and make a handsome profit even after paying severance." Interview with Ric Mentus, _Jamaica Daily News,_ March 7, 1976, p. 4.

3. In _A Voice at the Workplace_ (Andre Deutch, 1975) Michael Manley suggested that "In both the public and private sectors of the economy, experiments in worker participation in shop floor decisions should be commenced so that a foundation of experience in the processes of responsible worker democracy can begin."

4. See Carl Feuer, _Jamaica and Sugar Workers Cooperatives: The Politics of Reform_ (Ph.D. Diss. Cornell University, 1983), ch. 5.

5. Horace Levy, "What's Wrong with the Sugar Co-ops?" _Public Opinion,_ February 24, 1978.

6. As Stone points out, "Policy articulation in Jamaica is seventy percent symbol manipulation and thirty percent presentation of and accounting for government policy initiatives and programs." Carl Stone, _Democracy and Clientelism in Jamaica,_ (Transaction Books, 1980), p. 79.

7. In this and subsequent quotes, we have translated the Jamaican local language, Patois, from the original tapes to English.

8. Feuer, _op.cit.,_ p. 163.

9. _Ibid.,_ p. 164.

10. The Inter-American Foundation (IAF) is a liberal foundation that has supported numerous social reform projects in Latin America. It receives its funds from the United States Congress.

11. This marked an expansion for the Social Action Centre, which dropped its formal Jesuit affiliation and incorporated independently. At about the same time, lawyer Ronnie Thwaites became Chairperson of SAC.

12. Carl Stone teaches Political Sociology at the University of West Indies. Richard Fletcher, who is Michael Manley's brother-in-law, was later appointed head of the Sugar Industry Authority.

13. Evening classes were not feasible because the sugar workers were quite exhausted by the end of the day and because transportation was not readily available for evening travel.

14. See Feuer, op.cit., pp. 186 and 190.

15. Communication from Michael Manley's office, November 1984. Mr. Manley asked Mr. Fletcher to reply to some questions the authors had posed about the PNP government and the sugar workers cooperatives.

16. These three farms became cooperatives in 1978 when enough members had decided to join the cooperative organization.

17. Although women constituted a quarter of the work force at Frome and slightly less at the other two estates, they were under-represented on the Managing Committees. Between 10 and 20 percent of the committee members were women; no women ever served as Managing Committee Chairpersons.

CHAPTER III

COOPERATIVE PRODUCTION: THE STRUGGLE FOR A BETTER LIFE

Stand up, stand up, sugar workers and
work with all your might
The time has come for workers
to claim their legal right
But how can we obtain it
if we do not work
So let us come together
and work with willing hands.
(Benjamin Cornish, "Sugar Workers'
Song")

For the Jamaican sugar workers, life has always been hard. Eight hours a day, from seven o'clock in the morning until four in the afternoon, they work in the large wide-open fields with no shade to shield them from the scorching heat of the sun. When cutting seed cane among the tall-growing cane stalks, the workers must dress in long sleeves and pants so as not to get their skin blistered by the sharp green leaves. Fertilizers and herbicides burn their fingers and cause breathing problems. When the rains come women walk in watery mud up to the ankles covering the seed cane with hoes made heavy by the sticky mud. In the harvest time or "crop season," men must stoop low to cut the burned cane stalks close to the root, where the juice content is the highest. Many spend one or two hours a day walking or bicycling to and from the fields and their homes in the communities surrounding the estate lands. For the women, the day has already begun much earlier to give them time to cook breakfast, pack lunches, comb their children's or grand-children's hair, and tidy the house. When they come home there is supper to prepare and children to bathe before they can get some rest for the next days' toil.

The cane, on which the workers spend their energies and from which they eke out a meager livelihood, grows readily after being planted in mechanically prepared furrows, and doesn't need to be replanted for about seven years. An acre can yield as much as 50 tons of sugar cane, but only if the fields are carefully weeded, properly fertilized and irrigated, especially in the dry areas of the east. On the large estates, the fields had been allowed to deteriorate by their corporate owners in anticipation of selling off

60

the cane farms. The practice of burning the cane before cutting it, introduced in the 1960's to make manual harvesting easier, had left the soil impoverished and contributed to the general decline in productivity. In the first half of the 1970's the average yield was about 26 tons of cane per acre (1). Cane harvesting is back-breaking labor, even using the burning technique. The cutting begins around Christmas and ends sometime between June and August. Some of the cutters come down from the surrounding hills during the crop season and leave the estate when the harvest is completed. They live in dilapidated barracks provided by the estate. The other cutters and cultivators more often live in communities surrounding the estate lands. At Bernard Lodge, Monymusk and Frome, about one-quarter of the workers are women.

In the early seventies cane cutters earned about J$780 for the six-month harvesting season. The basic wage rate for cultivators was J$2.85 per day for men and J$2.50 per day for women (2). The crop season was a time of fairly regular work; a paycheck, however small, could be picked up every Friday. But after all the mature cane had been cut, grabbed by the mechanical loaders and hauled to the factory on trucks, the "dead season" began, and only a small number of workers were needed to service the fields. These were desperate times, when one had to beg the busha, (the farm manager) for work. For the sugar workers, cash to buy cooking oil, flour for dumplings, soap or a flask of rum was always in short supply. There was never enough for clothes, bus fare, examination fees, school lunches and uniforms for all of their children or grandchildren to go to school on a regular basis.

After the end of the harvest, their small savings were quickly used up, and the workers depended on neighborhood shopkeepers to extend them credit to obtain salt fish, rice and other basic necessities.

> From August going up to September, October, those were the days that were very bleak. Maybe there were special people that were given one or two days of work, but the whole rest, I mean the majority, had to stay home, because there was no work. Those were terrible days. (Beryl Davis)

The workers, always just barely making it, were never able to accumulate any savings. After wearing themselves out in the cane fields for forty or more years they could only look forward to a very small government pension.

After the cane is cut it is loaded by mechanical "grabbers" onto trucks and cane carts and brought to the factory to be washed, cut and crushed. The crushed cane is then pressed and drained of its juices, leaving the dry fibrous material -- bagasse -- which is used to generate heat for the enormous vacuum boilers in which the cane juice is boiled (3). When enough water has evaporated, a mixture of sugar and molasses is left, from which raw sugar is crystallized. For every ten tons of cane brought from the field to the factory, one ton of sugar is produced. Although over a quarter of the raw sugar remains in Jamaica, the bulk of it is shipped to England and the United States to be refined and marketed by the transnational sugar corporations headquartered there.

The field laborers saw little of the wealth created by the process of growing cane to maturity and transforming the cane stalk into sugar, rum and molasses. Even in 1975 when sugar commanded a record price of over J$600/ton, ten times its price a few years before, the basic pay rate for a cane cultivator was no more than J$5.30 a day (or about US$ 5.80).

Such were the conditions on the large estates when the Manley administration began to move the sugar industry increasingly under state control in the 1970's. The government-owned Frome Monymusk Land Company managed the assets of the three largest estates, Frome, Monymusk and Bernard Lodge. The government's National Sugar Company, established in 1975, owned 7 of the 12 remaining sugar factories on the island by 1978. The Sugar Industry Authority, a government controlled regulatory agency in existence since 1970, replaced the formerly very powerful and foreign-dominated Sugar Manufacturers' Association.

The Sugar Industry Authority (SIA) exerts substantial control over the sugar industry as a whole. It directs the marketing of sugar internally and for export, makes loans to cane farmers and sugar factories, proposes prices for cane and raw sugar to the

government, participates in the direction of the
publicly owned sectors of the sugar industry, produces
sugar industry statistics, publishes a trade magazine
and administers the Sugar Industry Research Institute.

The government's increasing control over the
sugar industry brought no improvements for the sugar
workers, however. On the estates managed by the
government, the conditions of the workers remained
unchanged. The workers continued to take orders from
the same staff inherited from the corporate owners;
economic insecurity, fear and humiliation continued to
be the order of the day. The Land Company executives
in Kingston were as invisible to the sugar workers as
the absentee owner "Mr. Charlie" was in the days of
slavery, and the board members, stockholders and
executive officers were when the estates were owned by
the West Indies Sugar Company (WISCO). The more
visible estate and farm-level staff continued to be
separated from the workers by a wide gulf of class,
color and cultural differences. Busha, the farm
manager, still decided where you would work, or
whether you would work at all. He could send you home
for being a few minutes late and of course you would
not collect any pay for that day. Any act of insub-
ordination, real or imagined, could be punished by the
loss of work and a diminished paycheck on Friday.

> At all times you had to submit your-
> self, humble yourself to them, regard-
> less of what they may do to you that is
> against your spirit. You just have to
> cope with it so as to keep in line so
> that you can get a livelihood. You
> have no expression or speech. Once you
> express yourself you are entirely
> thrown out. (Woman sugar worker, Frome)

Although the unions had somewhat improved the
lives of the sugar workers by collectively bargaining
for higher wages and by eliminating some of the most
grossly arbitrary practices by the bushas, they had
been unsuccessful in their efforts to increase job
security in the dead season. The fear of being denied
work was all-pervasive, usually preventing the workers' anger from erupting in front of their superiors.
Collective grievances were more readily confronted by
strike action (with or without the blessing of the

union officials), especially by the cane cutters who gained confidence from the critical nature of their task, finding security in their numbers. But unity, necessary for effective strike action, was often hard to come by in a system which allocated scarce jobs by favoring those most loyal to the busha.

The sugar workers found themselves working hard in the crop season day after day, month after month, year after year, in a job without prestige and, for many, filled with humiliation and fear. They worked with one narrow concern: how to wrest the most cash out of it to live without hunger and to secure a better future for their children and grandchildren. Their own poverty was made even more painful by the glaring inequities of the system. The busha and the other estate staff earned six to fifteen times what they did. The staff lived comfortably in brick or cement homes, with electricity and running water, equipped with appliances and nice furniture; the workers lived in shacks. Busha could afford a private car and was provided with a jeep on the job; most workers traveled on foot. The company allowed the busha to raise twenty or more head of cattle on company land; the workers could have none. He could vacation overseas and his children were sent to secondary schools and colleges; the children of workers often were too poor to attend school. He was buried in a fancy casket and was carried in a hearse to the cemetery, something the workers could never afford.

In offices in Kingston and overseas, the "Big Men" controlled the purse strings, allowing only a slight trickle to spill over to the sugar workers, the real producers of the cane. The workers had prepared the fields and planted the cane; they had weeded, watered and fertilized it; they had spaded the drains, reaped the cane and hauled it to the factory. Without them, there would be no cane and no sugar! And yet, what had they received for their years of back-breaking labor?

The organizers of the cooperatives and the worker leaders were hoping to change this situation. Their main concern was to make it possible for the sugar workers to increase their material well-being, to develop themselves as human beings and to find a sense of dignity and mental satisfaction which comes from heightened awareness, knowledge and the power to control one's own life. Cooperative control of the cane fields by the workers themselves would give them a stake in the cane cultivation process which would motivate them to give their best effort in nurturing the cane to maturity. Cooperative control would also give them the power to reset the priorities and to redistribute the fruits of their labor in a way which would give all of them economic security and better living conditions.

Cooperative Production

With the signing of the lease agreement in November of 1976, when the cooperators finally took over the full management of the cane fields, the co-op leaders knew that they were faced with an enormous challenge. First, they would have to make the cane cultivation process economically viable after almost a decade of continued losses under the former owners, WISCO, United Fruit Co. and most recently the government. Only through more efficient production could they hope to raise the material standard of living of the members in a substantial and lasting way. Second, they would have to radically restructure the plantation hierarchy, deeply entrenched since the days of slavery, to bring about a fundamental redistribution of resources and to improve the working conditions of the members. These changes would increase the productivity of the workers and would result in a prospering enterprise.

After the first year of operation of the three pilot farms, hopes were high for the other farms that were becoming co-ops. All three pilot farms had produced a modest profit. But at the same time, the optimism was tempered with caution. The worker leaders, the SAC organizers and advisors and government officials who had met at Trelawney Beach Hotel in 1975 had agreed that most of the newly added cooperatives would not be able to achieve viability unless the government took several steps to improve farming conditions, especially at Monymusk. Employment opportunities in areas other than sugar cane had to be created for surplus workers. Subsidies were necessary for irrigation, which at Monymusk was essential and very costly. A higher price would have to be paid to Monymusk growers for their cane in recognition of their higher cultivation costs. It was pointed out that the cooperatives would be faced with large losses in the beginning and that special loans from the Sugar Industry Authority would be necessary.

The 1976 crop was still technically under Frome Monymusk Land Company management, since the lease agreement was not formally signed until the fall of that year, and the cooperatives were not supposed to be charged for the cost of planting and tending the growing cane they took over. Instead, the Land Company charged the co-ops over J$13 million for the standing cane. The cooperatives insisted that they had been unfairly charged, but even after auditing adjustments J$7 million of that amount remained as a debt on the co-ops' books until they were disbanded in 1981. The accounts of the Land Company were so confused it was difficult to establish a clear financial picture for future projections. But it was abundantly clear that from the very beginning the financial position of the co-ops was weak, with equity capital sorely lacking.

To insure a sound financial structure, the cooperatives should have begun with an equity investment of J$12.5 million, according to one estimate (4). Actually, the only equity members had in the cooperative was from their shares of J$20 each, which amounted to J$100,000. The purchase of the farms was almost entirely debt financed (see Table 3.1). Lacking cash, the cooperatives were forced immediately to borrow millions of dollars of operating capital from commercial banks at interest rates as high as 14 percent. The burden of paying interest on such debts contributed heavily to continued losses (5).

The very weak financial situation was only one of a multitude of inherited problems which the cooperatives were expected to overcome. For the transnationals and the Land Company the main function of the cane lands had been to provide a steady supply of cane to the sugar factories. The losses incurred by WISCO and United Fruit Co. in the cultivation process (6) were offset by profits made in other sectors of their vertically integrated enterprises, such as shipping, insurance, refining and marketing. But the sugar worker cooperatives took over only the unprofitable part of the business, the cane lands.

TABLE 3.1: BALANCE SHEET OF COOPERATIVES AT START OF BUSINESS, 1976
(J$ Millions)

ASSETS		LIABILITIES	
Future crops	$ 5.0	Equity capital:	
Fixed assets	0.8	Member shares	$ 0.1
Inventories	1.0		
		Debt capital:	
Start-up costs (Non-crop expenses)*	3.7	Member severance deposits	$ 4.7
		SIA loan	2.9
		Owed to Frome/ Monymusk Land Company	2.8
Total assets:	$10.5	Total liabilities:	$10.5

*Includes $870,000 at Frome, $2,468,000 at Monymusk and $313,000 at Bernard Lodge.

SOURCE: Central Office Records

The factories were never integrated into the cooperative structure but remained under the management of the state-owned National Sugar Company. The efforts of the factory workers to gain control over the factories through a parallel cooperative movement were thwarted by government bureaucrats and politicians. The separation of the factories from the farms resulted in several difficulties for the cooperatives. The transnational corporations established a pattern in which their own estate lands would act as a buffer to keep the cane coming into the factories at times when other private farmers who also sold cane to the factories were unable or unwilling to supply them. For example, the private farmers would not supply any cane on weekends, because they wanted to avoid paying their workers premium rates (7). The cooperative leadership was squeezed from two sides. The rank and file cooperators, relying on weekend cutting as a major source of additional pay, exerted great pressure on their leadership to continue this pattern, sometimes refusing to cut on Thursday or Friday. The factories continued to look to the cooperatives to supply their weekend cane so they could operate without stopping. In addition, the factories severely limited the revenues of the cooperatives by frequent late starts in processing the sugar crop, by factory worker slowdowns and strikes, by machinery breakdowns, and by general management inefficiency. Factory-related problems meant that cane that had been burned was sometimes not accepted until days later. Such stale cane brought a lower price. Large amounts of cane were also left standing in the fields because of factory breakdowns (8).

Further, it was clear that the pressure to supply the factories with cane -- profitably or not -- also had led to the costly cultivation of marginal lands. The first General Secretary of the United Sugar Workers' Cooperative Council, Winston Higgins, analyzed four of the more productive farms on the three estates and concluded that between 30 and 80 percent of the acreage was yielding less than the break-even amount of 30 tons of cane per acre. He also suggested that to achieve profitability such unproductive lands should be withdrawn from cane production. The lease agreement, however, stipulated that the cooperatives were to grow cane on the leased land to guarantee an adequate supply of cane for the factories.

More problems were caused by cane fields and machinery that had been severely run-down by their previous owners. Much of the water-pumping system at Monymusk was worn out and inefficient, and many of its fields needed to be rehabilitated so they could better retain irrigation water. Most of the tractors on all three estates were old and worn out. To make the farms run efficiently, according to one co-op executive, about J$100,000 per farm would have been needed for irrigation equipment and another J$300,000 for tractors, amounting to J$9 million for all 23 farms. This was not counting the costs of investment in an irrigation system for Monymusk, nor some other expensive heavy equipment needed on each of the three estates.

The cooperatives also inherited an enterprise characterized by an oversupply of both workers and staff. One of the major reasons why WISCO and United Fruit Co. had been willing to sell the cane lands was that the main remedy to restore the profitability of cane cultivation, the mechanization of the harvesting process, was totally unacceptable to either a JLP- or PNP-controlled government. Mechanical harvesting would have added considerably to the island's already high unemployment of 23 percent in 1972. At the time of their formation, the cooperatives had to accept as members any workers then working on the three estates who wished to join, for fear of alienating the workers from the movement. The Tractor and Transport Departments were particularly burdened by excessive numbers, some 700 members and 100 staff.

The extremely weak financial position of the cooperatives and the organization of the sugar industry in Jamaica resulted in the co-ops' almost complete economic dependence on the Jamaican government and its Sugar Industry Authority (SIA). The SIA bought the cane from the cooperatives and paid them in two separate payments after the harvest (9). The crop was financed by a crop lien, a bank loan guaranteed by the government. The SIA undertook all the loan negotiations with the banks, excluding the cooperatives from even a token participation. Had the co-ops negotiated their own loans, they might have been more conscious of the true extent of their deficits, and the Managing Committees might have fought harder to cut such expenses as labor costs per ton and staff salaries and benefits. In the budgets we examined at Frome, there

was not even a line that specified each farm cooperative's cost of repaying interest and principal of
loans.

The inability of the co-ops to get credit without
government guarantees, and the fact that their losses
ultimately had to be subsidized by the government,
tied them to a number of government officials; this
was to have repercussions affecting even non-economic
areas of the cooperative enterprise. The majority of
the government and SIA bureaucrats, on whom the co-ops
depended, represented a relatively affluent upper-
middle-class outlook which was fundamentally antagon-
istic to the idea of worker control. There was little
interest among them in promoting policies which would
have reduced the dependence of the cooperatives on the
agencies controlled by them. Nor were they prepared
to develop supplements and alternatives to the sugar
industry, such as diversification into fish ponds,
beans, vegetables and tree crops, which could have
provided year-round employment for the cooperators.

No doubt the cooperators' effort to turn cane
cultivation into a profitable enterprise was an uphill
struggle from the very beginning. Just overcoming the
inherited obstacles to viability was in itself a
gigantic undertaking. But these problems were to be
compounded by a series of natural disasters, by cane
disease, by rapidly declining sugar prices, rampant
inflation, and a nationwide economic crisis, as well
as politically motivated obstructionism and sabotage.

Initial Accomplishments

Given the magnitude of the economic difficulties
besetting the cooperatives, their accomplishments in
the first three years of operation under co-op management were quite satisfactory.

The first crop under cooperative management was a
record crop for Frome, and represented an increase of
more than 12 percent over the previous year. Bernard
Lodge and Monymusk were hit with a severe drought, the
worst in 80 years. Production at Bernard Lodge
dropped by almost 30 percent, and at Monymusk by 38
percent, where the continuing problem with a deterior-
ating irrigation system aggravated the drought's
effect. Over the next two years, production was quite
good on all three estates, and productivity was well

70

within the average for the previous ten-year period (see Table 3.2).

Many cost-cutting measures were introduced. For example, the cost of running the USWCC main office in Kingston was half of the amount spent previously by the Land Company for the same purpose. Through a reduction of staff, the cost of staff benefits and salaries was cut by 20 percent. A whole new accounting system was developed which made farm-by-farm comparisons of expenditures possible. In addition, the old guarantee system' of cutting cane was abolished. Before, the cutters were paid on the basis of estimates of how much a cane field would yield, and consequently the cutters were often paid for cane that didn't exist. The cooperative leadership, against the opposition presented by the cutters, managed to introduce a system of paying the cutters for only the actual amount reaped, after the cane was weighed in at the weighing station. The cooperatives also changed the payment for some field operations, such as mechanical planting, from day labor to task work, when it was found that labor costs would be significantly reduced as a result. The new leadership also began a serious effort to stamp out widespread corruption, especially fraud, theft and kick-back schemes, inherited from the old system. Several staff were disciplined or fired after being found guilty of corrupt practices.

In spite of these measures, the co-ops continued to show a loss even though they managed to reduce their losses at Frome and Bernard Lodge in 1977 and 1978 respectively (see Table 3.2). USWCC General Secretary Higgins pointed out that in 1978 alone, the co-ops lost a total of almost J$5 million as a result of a large amount of standover cane, reduced juice quality resulting from stale cane and reaping done at premium pay rates. In that year 15,000 tons of cane were left unreaped in the fields because the factories were unable to process it when it was ready for harvest. This cost the co-ops over J$1.5 million. Given the long list of problems which the co-ops were burdened with from the beginning, plus the sharp increases in the cost of fuel, fertilizer and spare parts, the USWCC leadership could proudly assert that:

> To have reduced losses under such circumstances is a triumph for worker

71

TABLE 3.2: PRODUCTION, PRODUCTIVITY AND ESTIMATED LOSS
PER TON OF CANE, USWCC ESTATES 1976-1980,
WITH COMPARATIVE DATA FOR 1965-1974

Estate & Year	Production* (000's Tons)	Standover (000's Tons)	Productivity (Tons of Cane Per Acre)	Estimated Loss (Per Ton)
FROME				
1965-74 (average)	422	no data	32	no data
1976	403	0	30	$ 3
1977	454	0	34	2.5
1978	450	73	35	7
1979	441	189	30	9
1980	278	0	22	11
1976-80 (average)	405	52	30	6.5
BERNARD LODGE				
1965-74 (average)	215	no data	28	no data
1976	222	0	27	$ 6.5
1977	185	29	24	9
1978	252	43	31	4
1979	220	23	29	5
1980	173	19	25	9
1976-80 (average)	210	23	27	6.7
MONYMUSK				
1965-74 (average)	518	no data	31	no data
1976	439	0	28	$ 5
1977	271	0	23	19
1978	390	35	30	14
1979	351	45	27	22
1980	347	58	25	25
1976-80 (average)	360	28	27	17

*1976-80 production data includes standover cane, not reaped. This is jus-
tified since the cooperatives only controlled cane production and were
not responsible for the factory breakdowns and other problems that caused
large amounts of cane to be left unreaped.

SOURCE: Estate and central office records. Data for 1965-74 from
Vincent A. Richards and Allan N. Williams, "Some Institutional and Economic Aspects of the Jamaican Sugar Cooperatives," unpublished paper,
1981, Association for Caribbean Transformation, based on Sugar Industry
Research Institute, Annual Report, 1974.

management through the cooperative
structure on the sugar estates. (USWCC
Press Conference, March 27, 1979)

In the meantime, the government had failed to
provide any of the special assistance needed in
obtaining long-term financing or for improving the
irrigation system at Monymusk. Meeting after meeting
was held with officials from the Ministry of Agriculture, the Ministry of Finance and the SIA; plans were
made, but nothing was implemented.

Changes on the Farms

While these efforts were being made by the co-op
leadership and staff executives, the members saw a
number of changes occurring on the farms. The majority of the co-op members had a very limited understanding of the total financial picture of the cooperatives and were judging them on the basis of what they
could do to improve their own lives. For most of
them, the severance payment had been their main reason
for joining the co-op. The first half of the payment,
amounting to between J$500 and $2,000 for most members, was the largest sum of money they had ever seen
in their lives. It gave them the opportunity to
enlarge their homes or buy furniture, a motorcycle, a
few goats or pigs, or even a cow. In the first years
of the co-op they were looking forward to the return
of the second half of the severance payment that they
had lent to the organization to finance the original
purchase, and to profits from their enterprise.
Morale was high. According to Carl Stone, two-thirds
of members questioned at Morelands, the pilot co-op at
Monymusk, agreed that:

> ...work patterns had intensified to
> match the new responsibilities of
> worker self-management and the produc-
> tion of cane on the farm with a smaller
> labor force.

He continues:

> Members often had to take on new tasks
> while hitherto their job roles tended
> to be narrowly specialized. A new
> spirit of urgency affected work effort
> at most levels of production and espe-

73

cially among those working in groups
(10).

Some workers even did work that they didn't get paid
for; Norma Brown described her co-workers at Exeter
farm, Monymusk:

> If they go in the field, sometimes they
> pull grass and throw it out on the
> interval. If they are working in the
> field they don't say: "I don't get paid
> for this so I won't do it." They would
> do it along with the work billing the
> cane. (They would) pull it up and
> throw it out. They say they are
> benefiting from it. And if they go and
> see an animal in the cane they would
> catch it.

But at the same time, the cooperators, who had
all retained their union membership, insisted that
their wages and benefits should be based on union-
negotiated rates for the whole industry and were not
willing to sacrifice such short-term income in favor
of long-term cooperative development. In 1978 the
basic union-negotiated day-labor rate was increased
from J$5.30 per day to J$8.00 per day for men and
women, which kept them ahead of inflation, increasing
their real earning power (11). But the drought at
Bernard Lodge and Monymusk meant less work in the
harvest season, and thus less pay. The members were
still struggling to make a living, and their foremost
and always nagging problem was the continual shortage
of cash.

For many members this overwhelming concern with
money obscured the importance of many non-cash benefits which the co-ops provided for the membership.
The most significant one was the introduction of
guaranteed work in the `dead season.' Each member was
granted the right to work three days per week, which
not only increased the members' earnings from July
through December but also considerably lessened the
busha's hold over the workers. One of the older
cooperators, a member of the Central Board, Alexander
James, who had worked in the cane fields since Charlie's days' (i.e. before WISCO), talked about how he
had benefited from the co-op:

I was self-employed and I was proud of
that. I didn't go to ask anybody for
work. Work was provided for me and
most of all I was guaranteed employment, so I worked all the way through
(the year). When I didn't work it was
my own business why I didn't work. But
there was nobody to tell me that there
is no work for me to do. When a man is
self-employed he is a squire.

Another benefit for a large number of cooperators
was the use of land for members' homes, for gardens
and livestock pasture, and even for a burial ground.

When the co-op came in, they (the
members) had more land, they got more
land to work. Some of those edges and
gullies which were in cane during those
days, they could get it to work. About
a hundred or so (benefited). (Norma
Brown)

At Frome's Shrewsbury farm, some twenty members
cultivated a variety of vegetables for their own use
on one acre each of co-op land. A veritable `housing
development providing house sites for over a dozen
families emerged on another section of co-op land. At
Masemure, another Frome farm, at least thirteen
members cultivated small plots of land belonging to
the co-op. Many members on all three estates kept one
or several head of cattle and goats on the uncultivated intervals between cane fields and other grassy
sections of co-op land. Once a privilege reserved for
the staff, a sugar worker could keep cows; a few had
as many as eight or ten. Before the cooperative this
would have been beyond their means. Keeping one or
several cows was a form of savings for the members.
It enabled them to produce an occasional large amount
of cash; in 1981, selling a full-grown cow could bring
a price of J$1,000 or more. Getting access to the
uncultivated co-op lands was seen as an important
cushion against hard times:

In the earlier days, WISCO days, the
majority of lands would be planted in
cane. So if you didn't have a little
piece of land left by your parents, you
didn't have anywhere to plant. But now

75

> that the co-op came the co-op only
> planted on level ground, so the lands
> up there (on the hill) are being left
> uncultivated. Workers now cut it up bit
> by bit and they cultivate it. You can
> just go and take it as long as you
> cultivate it. So you see again, the
> co-op has brought in a vast expansion
> of call it agriculture business. And
> now you find the take-home pay may be
> small, but you have some backing all
> the way, so that the great amount of
> starvation that used to exist is no
> longer there. (Beryl Davis)

At one of the Monymusk farms, Salt Savannah, the members established a cemetery on co-op land when they had difficulties finding a burial spot for the deceased wife of a member. In the old days, i.e., before the co-op, all these activities would have been considered trespassing, and the workers would have been arrested had they tried to use the lands for their own needs.

Another very important benefit was the money granted the family to cover funeral expenses and the transportation provided to take the body to the mortuary and the cemetery. A Jamaican funeral is an elaborate event, preceded by a nine-night wake, for those who can afford it, with much eating, singing and dancing the geyrey (a dance traditionally performed at funerals). For the sugar workers, who lived their lives just barely meeting their basic needs, it was all the more important to be able to leave this life in style. The members always mentioned the funeral grant as one of the most important benefits brought through the co-op:

> In the old system if a worker died
> people would go to busha and say "Look
> Sam Stokes died on the corner yester-
> day" and busha would say "I'm sorry for
> him, he's dead" and that was all. They
> would not have anything to carry the
> body in to the grave. Or, busha would
> have a tractor and the tractor would
> carry the body. Now they have a
> hearse. The body will be put in the
> Sanford funeral parlour where busha

> would have gone if busha died. The
> hearse that would have carried busha
> now carries the member too. (Member
> Service Officer at Frome)

Not having been able to provide a family member with a
proper funeral was the ultimate reminder of one's
poverty and low status in society under the old
system.

A life insurance system for cooperators was put
into effect in 1976. A pension plan to supplement the
meager government pensions was on the drawing board
for years, but the General Secretary advised that it
should not be adopted due to a lack of co-op funds to
cover the plan. It was never put into effect (12). A
sick-leave policy was also prepared but rejected by a
majority of members, who preferred the system inherited from the Land Company. Members were paid sick
leave once a year, whether they were sick or not, but
would get no additional compensation if they were
actually sick or disabled.

The co-op also brought improved housing to many
members, although not to nearly as many as the co-op
leaders had hoped. Some empty homes on the farms were
rented to members by the cooperatives. But the main
effort to improve housing was provided by the PNP-controlled government through subsidized low-cost housing
development. Some of these homes were specifically
built for the workers in the sugar industry with funds
appropriated through the Sugar Industry Housing
Authority. A total of some one hundred sugar workers
(factory and field on the three estates) moved into
the homes made of cement, with two or three bedrooms,
indoor plumbing and a little yard. This was the dream
house of every sugar worker, most of whom were living
in small one- or two-room wooden shacks raised off the
ground on a pile of rocks.

The cooperatives created separate Member Service
Departments on each of the three estates, with Member
Service Officers helping members by informing them of
their rights, writing letters for illiterate members,
preparing tax and insurance forms, helping with
housing applications and funeral arrangements, visiting sick members and generally looking out for the
members' welfare. These officers were instrumental in
telling co-op members about the advantages of joining

77

the local credit union. The co-op provided collateral
for its members who took out loans and the option for
members to repay loans through payroll deduction.
Access to credit was a very significant benefit which
was unavailable before the co-op:

> It was only the Project Managers and
> the `Big Men' that knew about the
> credit union. But since the co-op came
> in, the Member Service Department and
> the credit union came around and
> encouraged us that we too as small
> people can be members of the credit
> union. The majority of us are members,
> so when a week comes when we find that
> the take-home pay will be small, we go
> to the credit union and get a loan. We
> find it very helpful. (Beryl Davis)

Perhaps the most important change of all was the
fact that the busha was no longer seen as the sole
source of one's well-being. One Member Service
Officer explained:

> There was a constant competition
> (between the co-op leaders and the
> Project Manager, i.e., the busha.)
> That was from the old system and the
> Project Manager knew whom he would give
> favors to. Good. But the people have
> a choice now, whether to go the busha
> or whether to go to the Managing
> Committee. Previously they didn't have
> a choice. And if busha didn't love
> them that was it. Now whether they are
> loved by busha or the Managing Commit-
> tee, they have to get it. All you have
> to do is to take it to the general
> membership and show that your mother is
> sick or your auntie is sick and if you
> can prove that it (the loan) is for a
> just cause, then you have to get it.
> Before you didn't have any choice. You
> couldn't take it to the union.

In their first few years of operation the cooperatives brought many material benefits to the members,
even though their cash income barely kept pace with
inflation (see Table 3.3). Most benefits were obtain-

TABLE 3.3: CONSUMER PRICE AND SUGAR WORKERS
WAGE INDEX COMPARISON 1974-1981

YEAR	CONSUMER PRICE INDEX	WAGE INDEX
1974	–	100
1974	112	186
1976	120	186
1977	135	186
1978	200	280
1979	250	280
1980	315	280
1981	–	337

SOURCE: Consumer Price Indices. Annual Review. Jamaica Department of Statistics, 1981. Wage Index calculated by
authors.

TABLE 3.4: USWCC 1980 PAYROLL, BY CATEGORY

Category	Number of Persons	Gross Pay Bill (in Million $)	% of Total
Farm worker members	4000 (est)	J$ 8.5	60
Service Dept. members*	700 (est)	J$ 4	27
Staff**	241	J$ 2	14
TOTAL	4941 (est)	J$ 14.5	100

* Includes Tractor and Transport Department and Irrigation
Department members.
** Excludes education staff paid through grant funds from the Inter-
American Foundation.

SOURCE: Central Office files.

ed through the initiative of the co-op leadership and did not require any major increase in the budget. Given the lack of financial support from the government for capital improvement of irrigation, transportation equipment and for a reduction of the debt burden, the attempts to achieve viability and improved living standards were a frustrating fight for the co-op leadership.

Even more frustrating were the continued inequalities between the co-op members and their employed staff. A major goal of the co-op was to reduce the wide gulf between the two groups through a more equitable distribution of income and benefits. But the staff used their technical expertise as leverage and their connections with top officials of the Frome Monymusk Land Company to get a contract guaranteeing them employment for 22 months. They continued to be paid by the Land Company and the cooperative in turn paid the Land Company for their services. They also collected their full severance pay which for some amounted to over J$20,000. Unlike the sugar workers who had to become co-op members to retain their employment and who had to invest half their severance money in the business, the staff were given the option of not joining the cooperative and thus did not have to invest one cent in the enterprise.

At the expiration of their 22-month contract, the staff negotiated a new contract that virtually guaranteed life-time tenure with no reduction in salaries or benefits for those whom the cooperators agreed to retain in their employ. In 1980, the typical Project Manager, i.e., the busha, earned J$9-10,000 per year, the other field staff earned about J$7-8,000, and the average member earned about J$2,400 a year. Higher level executives were paid between J$20-30,000 per year. In 1980, the total cost of salaries alone for the 241 staff members employed by the co-op amounted to J$2 million (see Table 3.4). The staff also received free housing, free electricity, a cooking gas allowance, sickness and vacation leave, pension benefits, and pasture for livestock. These benefits averaged over 50 percent of their salaries and added at least J$1.2 million to the cost of maintaining the staff. Thus, the employee salaries and benefits contributed heavily to the mounting deficits. The members began to ask -- with good reason -- how they could be the owners of the business, when they were earning only a fraction of what their own employees, the staff, were paid.

For some co-op members the gap between themselves and the lower echelon staff was narrowed significantly. These were workers who became Estate Board chairpersons and the Central Board members who had access to co-op owned cars, Senior Member Service Officers who were paid a salary of J$5,000 per year and were given the use of a jeep, and those members who were appointed farm "accountants", i.e., bookkeepers, or supervisors in the Tractor and Transport Departments. At Monymusk, Managing Committee chairpersons and the supervisors (who were over-represented on the committees) also became increasingly differentiated from the rest of the membership by receiving larger wage increases and by securing for themselves estate housing left vacant by former staff.

Other inequalities within the membership persisted in the cooperative period and the elimination of these was not given much emphasis by the leadership, preoccupied as it was much of the time with trying to keep the co-ops afloat financially. Women members continued to earn much less than the men (see Table 3.5). This was primarily due to the fact that the highest paid male members were the cutters, the watchmen, the trailer loaders, tractor and transport drivers and mechanics. These were all jobs that were rarely (in the case of cane cutting) or never performed by women. Women who did a disproportionate amount of the cultivation work were more often paid as day laborers than as task workers, although a woman who preferred task work could usually get it. Women were less often called to work on premium paying days, since cultivation work was rarely beset with the kind of urgency which would have required them to work on Saturdays and Sundays. On the whole, women cooperators did not feel that they were being discriminated against with regard to income and benefits because they accepted the existing division of labor. For example, the fact that only a few women on each farm worked as cane cutters was a result of choice rather than any explicit discriminatory rule. Some of the women supervisors at Frome did complain about wage discrimination and with good reason: their annual earnings were generally at least J$1,000 lower than those of their male colleagues, while the nature of their work was identical.

81

TABLE 3.5: MEMBER INCOME, BY SEX, AT THREE FROME FARMS, 1980*

	SHREWSBURY				ALBANY				MASEMURE			
	Number		Percent		Number		Percent		Number		Percent	
	W	M	W	M	W	M	W	M	W	M	W	M
$3800 or more	0	11	0	9	0	10	0	9	0	7	0	6
3000–3799	1	26	2.5	22	2	15	5	13	2	13	4	12
2500–2999	6	30	17	26	7	20	17	18	5	17	10	15
2000–2499	14	21	39	18	13	23	1	20	19	26	40	24
1500–1999	14	18	39	15	16	24	38	21	19	24	40	22
1499 or less	1	12	2.5	10	4	22	9	19	3	23	6	21
TOTAL	36	118	100	100	42	114	100	100	48	110	100	100

*Includes members who worked the last week or two of the year.

SOURCE: Farm payroll records

The Manley administration initiated two laws of special significance for women workers: one was the law guaranteeing equal pay for equal work for women and men; the other was the Maternity Leave (With Pay) Act of 1979 providing job security and a minimum of three months leave including two with full pay. Many cooperators believed that these added benefits were provided by the cooperatives, although in reality they applied to all Jamaican workers.

Work Organization

Even though the co-ops were largely unsuccessful in bringing about a significant redistribution of income and benefits in favor of the cooperators, they did bring some important changes into the day-to-day work organization and management structure of the farms. This was all the more noteworthy since it was the feeling of humiliation and powerlessness that stood out the most clearly in people's minds when they talked about pre-co-op days:

> One of the key reasons why I supported the co-op from the start was because it was suggested that if the co-op came on stream you wouldn't have any boss. You couldn't be pushed around anymore. You would be self-employed, and that was one of the things that gave me the courage to take up the challenge, and so I did. (Alexander James)

For many reasons it became a major struggle to change work conditions. Several groups whose socio-economic or political positions were threatened by the cooperative movement, such as opposition party members, factions of the ruling PNP, some government officials, union leaders and especially the co-op staff, were determined to prevent full worker control over the cooperative. Accustomed to taking orders from the busha all their lives, the sugar workers themselves found it difficult to believe that they could run and control a multimillion-dollar business. In addition, the co-ops inherited the old estate structure and its personnel. Thus, the structure of the co-op was not sufficiently different from the old plantation system to force a drastic change in the members' perception of themselves in relationship to their former bosses.

In the old system, before the co-op, the day-to-day work operations on each farm were carried out either by work gangs or by individuals performing work paid at a task rate. Operations were divided into harvesting and cultivation work, and while most members specialized in one or the other category, some members were more versatile. For example, a man could specialize in spade work, (digging and cleaning drains), but during those dry periods of the harvest season when there was no spade work to be done, he could work as a cane cutter in a reaping gang. Some men would only cut cane and do no other work at all on the farms in the `dead season'. The majority of the women belonged to various cultivation gangs and would rotate between fertilizing, weeding, planting and supplying tasks. A few women specialized in cutting dribble (short cane pieces for planting), and a handful of women would harvest as well. Fertilizing the fields and cooking lunch for the workers remained exclusively female tasks, whereas spraying herbicides and driving tractors was done by men only. Some of the gangs were exclusively female, with female supervisors, or drivers. Others were mixed or all male, as in the case of most of the harvesting gangs, and were usually supervised by male supervisors, or headmen. In addition to the registered cooperative members, occasional laborers, or so-called butterfoot, would be hired from time to time.

The supervisors were selected by the busha, and did not have to do any manual labor. When day labor was performed, the supervisors would simply make certain that the workers were working and check on the quality of work. When task work was carried out, they would also measure the number of rows planted, weeded or cut and record it for the bookkeeper, who would calculate the proper pay for each worker. The day-to-day management of the farm was in the hands of the busha, his two assistants, and the bookkeeper. The bookkeeper prepared the weekly payroll. The busha and his assistants were in charge of the overall technical and financial management of the farm. The busha also acted as the liaison with higher level staff -- the Agricultural Superintendent, the Area Manager, the Crop Control Officer and the Chief Executive of the estate.

This old system of organizing work encouraged narrow specialization, laxity, opportunism and distrust among the workers. It was also characterized by poor management, entirely lacking in comparative farm budgeting and cost control and marred by kick-back schemes and fraud. This was the system of work organization inherited by the cooperatives. However, some significant changes did occur in the day-to-day conditions of work.

Since the workers were now, at least in theory, the owners of the enterprise, they could not be easily dismissed by their farm manager. They could only lose their right to work through a decision to strip them of their membership made by a majority of the members of their primary farm cooperative. This, coupled with the guaranteed three days of work in the out-of-crop season, gave members a measure of security previously unknown to them. Before the co-ops, the unions would defend a worker and protect him or her against arbitrary dismissal but workers generally agreed that it was hard to win against the busha. Now the busha (renamed Project Manager under the co-ops) had less power over them.

Another significant change in work conditions had to do with the way work was scheduled. Each week, work schedules were made up by the Project Manager together with workers elected to the Managing Committee. Before, no ordinary workers had been involved in this process, only the staff. Unfortunately, this did not eliminate the opportunity for the Project Managers to continue to use favoritism in allocating work, since those committee members who would make up the work schedules with the Project Manager were usually also supervisors. There were numerous cases observed at Frome of members getting a nice piece of work, or more work than others, or even work as the Project Manager's servant, as a reward for loyalty to him.

Favoritism was counteracted by the co-op leadership and the progressive members, who at Monymusk and Bernard Lodge managed to institute a new system in which the members selected their own supervisors. At Frome, where the members lacked enough organizational strength for this, the leadership instead tried to eliminate favoritism by requesting detailed monthly work schedules from the Project Managers. They also requested that these schedules be made available to the Managing Committees so that the committees could check on how much and what kind of work had been

85

allocated each member. This would have exposed
favoritism and would have allowed the Managing Committees to intervene more effectively on behalf of the
members. The staff, however, refused to comply. At
Frome, then, the only way to counteract the Project
Manager's control over the allocation of work was to
bring a grievance to the Chairperson or a member of
the Managing Committee, who would then pressure the
Project Manager to change his behavior. Or an individual could insist forcefully on his or her right to
refuse or take a particular job. One woman Managing
Committee member put it this way:

> Those (the staff) are the people from
> WISCO days, so they still go on the
> opportunity of oppressing. Now when
> you go up there and you say "I want a
> little work" and he (the Project
> Manager) says "No, I don't have any
> work to give you," I say "Look Sir,
> such and such a field needs to be
> weeded". You show him where there is
> work. He can't tell you that you can't
> do it. He has to say "You go and do
> it". I can stand up and defend myself
> and show him what I am talking about.
> You can use your rights, they can't do
> a thing, but if you allow them, they
> will do as in former days. So I
> believe that you must be strong-minded,
> you must be willing to stand up. As
> Bob Marley says: Stand up, get up,
> stand up for your rights. (Beryl Davis)

Another gain for the members was the right to refuse a
job which was considered too heavy or dirty, or task
work which would be so hard that too little could be
earned given the rate of pay for the task.

> Now that the co-op has come in, it is a
> far different thing, because if the
> Project Manager says to you "Look, go
> and move that truck" and you say "I'm
> not moving that truck," he'll say "All
> right" and he will find someone who
> will move the truck instead of you.
> That is a big edge I have over him. In
> former days you couldn't do things like
> this. (Beryl Davis)

In former days, refusing a job would mean getting no work at all for that day or being forced to do it against one's will.

Although this change represented an advantage to the individual members, it had some negative consequences for the cooperative. On one hand, it made it necessary to hire a large number of non-members or "butterfoot" for jobs that the members did not want. On the other hand, as long as refusal to perform a particular task was primarily seen in terms of staff versus member power to control the production process, it inhibited the growth of new work ethic based on a concern for the good of the collective.

Yet another advance for the members was the more relaxed atmosphere on the job; removed was the threat of losing one's job for trivial violations of work rules. For example, in pre-co-op days a person arriving even a minute or two late for work would not get any work at all that day. Nor was anyone on day labor permitted to leave before four o'clock even when the work allocated for that day had been completed. The cooperative allowed occasional tardiness, and the members who worked by the day were allowed to go home when the job was finished.

The most important change was that some members were gaining knowledge and information about their business. The Chairpersons of the Managing Committees would meet the Project Managers at least once a month to go over the next month's budget, reaping targets and cultivation plans. The Estate Boards and the Central Board had access to data about all three estates. Farm-by-farm costs and budgets were available, and this allowed the co-op leaders, and thus the sugar workers, for the first time in the history of the Jamaican sugar industry to make informed decisions about the production of cane. Also for the first time, the sugar workers had, through their leaders, direct access to the SIA, the Ministry of Agriculture and the Cooperative Department, and occasionally even to the Prime Minister himself.

A further benefit of vital importance to the members and the democratic operation of the cooperatives was education. In the first few years, the Member Service Officers (most of whom had been chosen from among the Social Action Centre organizers) continued to develop programs and seminars for the general membership, with the help of SAC. Funds for a large-scale program including literacy training were sought from the Inter-American Foundation in Washington. This effort was delayed until late 1979 because of opposition from the Jamaican government, a topic we shall return to in chapter five. In spite of the late implementation of a comprehensive education program, some two-hundred members selected on the basis of interest benefited from courses within Jamaica, from scholarships to study cooperative development in Israel, Canada, or Hungary, or from short visits to Panama or Cuba.

Another Break With the Past

Even before the cooperatives were established, it was clear to the SWCC organizers and SAC that it would be necessary to diversify production to achieve viability while also providing work for the members in the dead season. The workers at Bernard Lodge were pioneers in planting food crops.

As early as 1976, the cooperators at Windsor Park farm decided to grow rice during the out-of-crop season. The first harvest from eighteen acres yielded 44,000 pounds. Subsequently, the members increased the number of acres in rice at the farm and also planted peanuts, plaintain, coconuts, bananas, cassava, beans, okra and corn (13). At the suggestion of one of the workers, Harold Badjoo, cane irrigation water was recycled and used for the rice paddies (14). March Pen farm put in a fish pond and was also growing beans, cucumbers and rice. Reid's Pen farm constructed a two-acre fish pond in July 1979 and six months later began harvesting African Perch (15). At Monymusk, five acres were planted in pumpkins and tomatoes in 1977. Diversification made slower headway at Frome, perhaps because many of the members there had access to small plots of land of their own. At Frome farm on the Frome estate poultry raising was begun in 1978. It yielded a small profit the first year but was abandoned after the second year because the cost of the feed exceeded the income from the sale of the chickens. The members still benefited because the chickens were sold to them well under going market prices.

Because of the co-ops' lack of capital, these projects remained too small to significantly contribute additional income or out-of-crop employment for the members, but they represented an important break with the past. A dent was made in the several hundred-year-old practice established by the British colonial regime of using Jamaica's best agricultural lands and greatest capital investment for sugar to sweeten other people's tea, instead of producing food for Jamaican stomachs. With one or two exceptions, the diversification efforts were initiated by sympathetic outsiders and some co-op leaders and members. Funds were obtained from a variety of sources, among others Oxfam, the Dutch government and Canadian University Services Overseas.

Although there was a clear recognition among government officials that diversification was needed, no major effort was launched through their initiative. The Ministry of Agriculture did some feasibility studies on growing non-cane crops for several Monymusk farms in 1978, but made no effort to redistribute funds for sugar cane cultivation into other agricultural crops. The government officials continued to view the cooperatives as cane suppliers for the sugar factories and cited the lease agreement under which the cooperatives had agreed to continue to grow sugar cane and the lack of financial resources as the two main obstacles to diversification on a larger scale.

Mounting Problems

Although much had been accomplished in the way of cutting costs and making life more bearable for the members, the cooperatives continued to lose money. The government had not provided any of the special assistance which it had agreed in 1975 was necessary to get the co-ops on a sound financial footing. For example, the SIA had concluded in a report that

> In the case of Monymusk the estimated accumulated losses are so large that the interest burden completely swamps all profits envisaged. It is therefore assumed that a Special Programme Loan will be made available of $6.6 million by the SIA (16).

In 1979, the General Secretary of the co-ops concluded that "nothing has been done yet" with regard to Monymusk's irrigation problems. The Minister of Agriculture, A.U. Belinfanti, more than once publicly promised to get improvement in the irrigation system of the Monymusk region. Nothing, however, was ever actually done about it. Long-term, low-interest financing was constantly requested by the cooperatives. Stop-gap crisis financing through higher interest, short-term commercial loans was all they received.

In 1978, the cooperatives faced their first major crisis when it was time to return the severance deposits to the members. At a meeting involving top government and union officials a decision was made not to repay the money, because the government lacked sufficient funds. This caused the co-ops irreparable harm by undermining the members' confidence not only in their own leadership but in the PNP government as well (see Chapter IV). The members were beginning to feel betrayed. In 1979, for the third year in succession, the co-ops showed no profits. In the same year the accumulated losses coupled with the lack of adequate government support had made their financial situation intolerable. The USWCC General Secretary described the situation as follows:

> USWCC sugar cooperatives are unable to plant the new 1980 crop or to <u>maintain the crop</u> in the ground, because not enough money is being made available. The Crop Lien Loan for 1980 is being <u>withheld</u> because Ministry of Finance has declined to give the usual letter of comfort to guarantee the loan. The Production Incentive Loan or Replanting Loan of $450,000 is not being made available to USWCC by the Sugar Industry Authority (SIA) even though the work has been done, inspected and certified. Without this loan creditors cannot be paid.

> The only money available is the first payment of $15 per ton on the cane that we are delivering to the factories daily. This money is just enough to keep further reaping going.

We repeat that <u>no cultivation, planting or maintenance</u> is being done and many workers are not getting any weekly wage at all."(17)

The USWCC once again asked the government to fulfill the agreements and proposals of the Prime Minister's Committee of 1975 and the plans developed by the SIA. They wanted the immediate release of a replanting loan and the issue of a letter of comfort to the bank to secure the Crop Lien Loan. They also demanded a solution to the long-term financing of its debt.

Although much of the government's inactivity with regard to its full support of the co-ops is no doubt attributable to bureaucratic inefficiency, incompetence and the unwillingness of some top officials to seriously assist the cooperatives in becoming less dependent on the government, it is also true that by 1979 the Jamaican economy as a whole was in serious trouble. The government could no longer provide crop lien loan guarantees even had it wanted to, because in 1978 it had signed a new agreement with the United States dominated International Monetary Fund (IMF) which imposed a number of conditions on the Jamaican government in return for a US$240 million loan. Among the conditions was the prohibition on guaranteeing any new private loans such as the crop lien loan guarantees that had previously been made by the government on behalf of the cooperatives. The co-ops were forced to rely solely on their cane sales to finance the reaping, and all of the operations had to be scaled down. The SIA itself was having cash-flow problems and the sugar factories continued to show substantial losses.

In late 1979, the cooperatives' financial situation had become desperate. While maintaining normal allocation of staff benefit monies, the executive staff had resorted to using payroll deductions of co-op members' contributions to National Housing Trust, insurance, Sugar Industry Housing, etc., to cover operational expenses. This was done over the objections of the Central Board members. Some cooperators could not collect insurance benefits, because their payments had not been forwarded to the insurance company. Throughout the next year, conditions continued to deteriorate.

Emphasizing the co-ops' economic significance in the Jamaican economy, various government officials affirmed the need to get the cooperatives on a more favorable economic footing. Wesley Wainright, the Chairman of the SIA, at a Central Board meeting in February 1980 asserted that the SIA had to help the co-ops as much as possible since they produced some 30 percent of the island's cane, and he recognized that the future of the cooperatives depended upon the efficiency of the factories. He also agreed to assist the co-ops with a replanting grant, rather than a loan. But in March and April, SIA officials concluded that no money was available. Co-op spending had to be restricted to proceeds from weekly cane sales. No funds were available for on-going expenses and the creditors were pressing for payments. The 1980 crop, the poorest of all co-op harvests, was some 100,000 tons less than the disastrous crop of 1977 which had resulted from the drought at Monymusk and Bernard Lodge. At Frome, the crop was particularly small and productivity had reached an all-time low of 22 tons per acre. In addition to the general lack of funds which had kept field operations down to a minimum, the flood of 1979, cane disease, poor weed control, illicit fires and livestock damage had taken their toll.

According to SIA and National Sugar Company officials, the main problems at Bernard Lodge and Monymusk were the continuing difficulties with cane haulage (18), shortage of spare parts, tires and tubes, and factory breakdowns and slowdowns that made them unable to receive all of the co-op cane.

For the sugar workers, all these problems boiled down to one essential fact: the hopes they had had for more income were unfulfilled at the end of every crop. For most of them, no profits had ever materialized. What was worse, with the mounting crisis, the extra payments for vacation and sick leave, the after-crop bonus and retroactive wage increases, could not be paid on time. The members became increasingly demoralized.

Those who firmly held that the business was theirs continued to work hard and conscientiously. They were convinced that the cooperatives would succeed in the long run. But the majority of members were losing interest in their work. A number of factors contributed to this situation: the failure of most of the co-ops to make a profit and to return the members' severance deposit; the belief of many that even if their own farm were successful, their effort would be mitigated by losses incurred elsewhere; the feeling of many that they didn't really own the business; the continued struggle between co-op members and the staff in enforcing discipline; and the lack of discipline and commitment to the co-op among the staff in general.

The discipline problem need not have become a serious one had the issue of who was actually in control of the farm, the Managing Committee or the Project Manager, been resolved. As things stood neither wanted to alienate the membership, or at least not those members loyal to them, by acting as a disciplinarian. Without an effective system for enforcing discipline when fear of losing employment was no longer an incentive for doing well and when many cooperators did not see the business as truly theirs, selfishness and opportunism continued to find fertile ground among the members. The old plantation structure had led people to tacitly accept corruption as a normal part of the system. Thus, the objective conditions of day-to-day work were never sufficiently changed to unleash the members' energy and creativity. Their initiative remained stifled.

The discipline problem among the members was not nearly as severe as among the staff, however. The members were paid by the day or by task; they were supervised out in the field and had to expend a certain amount of effort to continue to get paid. The staff, on the other hand, had the best of all worlds. Regardless of job performance, they retained all their material privileges, were paid by the month, and remained generally powerful enough to escape any form of effective discipline by their employers, the co-op members. As a result, the farms continued to suffer productivity losses due to insufficient weed control and irrigation, illicit burning of cane to ensure premium time cutting and damage by livestock belonging to members and staff.

The demoralization of the members was further aggravated by the worsening economic conditions outside the co-op and a growing feeling that the government's policies were not helping the "small man." As part of the IMF agreement, the Jamaican government had been forced to set up a tight austerity program restricting imports and wage increases, reducing government spending and devaluing the Jamaican dollar (19). Prices increased; consumer commodities such as cooking oil, rice, flour, and soap became scarce; consumer demand dropped as a result of a restricted wage policy; and all this led to the financial collapse of various enterprises and an increased loss of jobs. Many cooperators by 1980 had lost all hope that the PNP government would return their severance deposit. There didn't seem to be any expectation of making a profit, and many felt they would never see their money unless there were some drastic changes in conditions. The political opposition, the JLP, had plenty of fuel for their fire: "PNP mismanagement!" they cried. The PNP government fought back, accusing JLP-supporting businessmen of hoarding goods and deliberately creating shortages to discredit the government. The PNP was clearly on the defensive.

The Co-ops Fight Back

The most dedicated co-op leaders and supporters tried their best to keep up the morale of the members and to take constructive steps to improve their economic condition. Several more diversification projects were started in 1979 and 1980. At Bernard Lodge two fish ponds were constructed and the cultivation of beans, cassava, pumpkins and onions was to begin at six Monymusk farms. Plans were also made for the construction of six fish ponds covering 20 acres at one of the Monymusk farms. A fish pond and a peanut cultivation project were started on two farms at Frome. The cooperators of Belle Isle and Albany farms at Frome enthusiastically began digging the pond and preparing the field even before they had received the small grant from an American Quaker organization, Right Sharing of World Resources, to fund the two projects (20). The pond was dug under the supervision of Alfred Bahadour, the Chairman of the Belle Isle Managing Committee, over the protests of the Area Manager who claimed that it was located too near his house. After the successful completion of the pond Belle Isle had to wait for over one year for the government fishing agency to stock it. At Albany, Beryl Davis, the Estate Education Committee Chairperson, led a large group of women volunteers in preparing the field for peanut cultivation. Certainly there were still co-op members who had kept their faith in the cooperative and who were willing to work hard, with or without pay, to save it.

Efforts were made to deal with high costs associated with the service branches, especially Tractor and Transport (T&T). These units accounted for over one-fourth of the total co-op payroll in 1980. The expense of their services was borne by the farms on each estate (see Table 3.4). The Monymusk T&T unit had cost so much that the USWCC Central Board decided, in 1980, to split it off from the cooperatives and transfer it to the government-owned National Sugar Company. With the change of government in that same year, the plan was never implemented. A comprehensive cooperative education program finally got under way in 1980, after years of fighting against efforts by the Ministry of Agriculture to control it. Bernard Lodge invited the Social Action Centre to conduct an organization development program aimed at improving the financial viability of the estate. This program was later expanded to include Monymusk as well. Because of the dissolution of the cooperatives by the JLP government the organization development program was never completed. Even so, it was clear in the fall of 1981 that a new system of budget control instituted through the organization development process had led to significant reductions in the cost of production, especially for supervisory personnel and labor overhead costs.

It was a struggle against overwhelming odds. In October of 1980, parliamentary elections were held amidst economic distress and politically induced violence. For the cooperatives, the election victory of the Jamaica Labour Party spelled the beginning of the end. The cooperatives were not operating in a vacuum but as a part of Jamaican society and the world economy. Many of their economic problems were caused by a faltering national economy. The power struggles inside the co-ops, which seriously hampered their economic performance, were largely consequences of the plantation system and of the class structure of Jamaican society in general. Despite their valiant efforts, the sugar workers never had complete control of their own enterprise.

1. World Bank, Staff Appraisal Report. Sugar Rehabilitation Project. Jamaica, January 19, 1978, p. 6. Burning the cane reduces the sugar content of the stalks because of an added delay of 12 hours to several days between burning and cutting, according to this report (p.21).

2. In 1969 J$1.00 = US$1.20; in 1976 J$1.00 = US$1.10.

3. In an efficient factory, bagasse burning provides almost all the necessary energy for this process. To the extent that the machinery is inefficient, the factories must burn imported oil, thus raising the cost of sugar production.

4. Winston C. Higgins, "United Sugar Workers' Cooperative Council, Limited. Discussion paper on improvement of co-operatives." October 25, 1978, p. 5.

5. The General Secretary of the cooperatives, Winston Higgins, claimed that the cooperatives paid over J$3 million in interest alone in 1978.

6. According to the 1971 Annual Report of WISCO, then owner of Frome and Monymusk estates, the losses for that year amounted to J$1.3 million. The reasons given for the poor performance included staff unrest, poor cultivation practices, failure to maintain adequate replanting and ineffective field supervision.

7. The premium time pay rate was 1.5 times the daily rate on Saturday and 2 times the daily rate on Sunday.

8. In 1970-74, an average of 13.8 percent of availble grinding time in Jamaican sugar factories was lost as a result of stoppages caused primarily by mechanical, electrical and steam generation failures. Sugar Industry Authority Annual Reports, quoted in Carl Feuer, Jamaica and Sugar Worker Cooperatives: The Politics of Reform. (Ph.D. Diss., Cornell University, 1983) p. 100.

9. The SIA paid cane producers by sugar content of the cane. It paid J$18 per ton of cane in 1976;

by 1980 it was paying them J$32 per ton, assuming 10 tons of cane yielded 1 ton of sugar.

10. Carl Stone, "The Morelands Sugar Cooperative." *Jamaica Sugar Digest*, #123, 1976, p.9. The study included some 80 of a total of 200 members at Morelands.

11. The Manley government introduced equal pay for women and men in 1975.

12. In contrast, staff members continued to be covered by pensions, paid for by the cooperatives.

13. *Workers Time*, 2/3-4, March-April 1977.

14. *Workers Time*, 3/2, March-April 1978.

15. The first batch of 1000 pounds of fish was sold to the government's Agricultural Marketing Corporation at J$.85 per pound. If the cooperative had been capable of selling the fish directly at retail, they would have brought in at least J$2.00 per pound.

16. Sugar Industry Authority, "Sugar Industry Rehabilitation Programme," quoted in Winston C. Higgins, Press Conference Statement by United Sugar Workers' Cooperative Council, March 27, 1979, p. 3.

17. Press Conference Statement by United Sugar Workers Cooperative Council, March 27,1979, pp. 9-10.

18. Much of the haulage equipment was old and worn down and was frequently breaking down.

19. By 1979 the Jamaican dollar had plunged to U.S. $0.57 from U.S. $1.10 in 1976.

20. Co-author Frank Lindenfeld helped the two Frome farms in locating and applying for these funds. As part of the same proposal, March Pen Farm at Bernard Lodge also applied for money to build a fish pond. The grant applications were made through the Social Action Centre.

CHAPTER IV

WORKER CONTROL: FACT AND FICTION

> It is very difficult when you are
> dependent on the government as is the
> case with the sugar industry. So how
> can you be in that situation and not
> get into politics a little bit? It was
> hard. (Matthias Brown)

Turning theoretical worker ownership of the
cooperatives into actual worker control was a tortuous
process. Again, as in the effort to achieve economic
viability, the sugar workers were saddled with old
baggage, which continued to weigh them down. Much of
the former management structure was retained. Although the workers' Managing Committees were officially in charge, the busha (now Project Manager) was
still on the farm. The estates were integrated into a
centrally regulated sugar industry and were economically dependent on the government. The government
bureaucrats were steeped in neo-colonial thinking and
behavior, and the workers were limited by widespread
illiteracy and lack of formal education.

Furthermore, the sugar co-ops remained a relatively isolated instance of cooperative development in
Jamaica and they thus had few allies. A serious
effort to organize worker cooperatives at the three
estate sugar factories (by that time owned by the
government's National Sugar Company) was launched by
the Social Action Centre in 1976. Organizing committees were established in the factories, and even some
factory staff supported the cooperative idea. The
farm cooperative organizing group, the SWCC, saw the
spread of worker control to the sugar factories as a
political necessity (See box, following page). But
the organizing efforts were blocked by a coalition of
the top factory executives and the dominant center/
right wing of the People's National Party (PNP).
Prime Minister Manley himself supported workers'
participation in management but not their control of
the factories.

The administrative separation of the previously
integrated factories and fields led to poor coordina-
tion between the two, contributing substantially to
the cooperatives' economic difficulties. The inabil-

THE POLITICAL GOALS OF THE SWCC*

"The longer range goals of the SWCC include control of the whole sugar industry (factories and other large farms included) and mobilization of other workers and small farmers towards a thorough-going agricultural reform...It is not enough to speak of 'worker participation' -- what the workers require in justice is 'control'. As long as a few capitalists or bureaucrats are making the final decisions, there can never be justice for the workers. We have chosen the cooperative system of running our farms because the most basic cooperative principle is the equal right of every worker-member to be involved in decision-making, in social development, and in sharing the surplus...

"Especially in the sugar industry, there is a disproportionate amount of profit accruing to the manufacturers and shippers, and the farmers must come to share this and not forever be left with the hardest and least fruitful tasks. Farm workers and factory workers must unite together for control of the whole sugar industry...

"The SWCC will not even rest satisfied when the whole sugar industry comes under worker control, but will seek to throw its full support behind other workers' and peasants' movements for control over the land, over services provided, and over marketing of goods. We will use our resources to promote a just and equal system of land distribution, and we will fight against all capitalist and bureaucratic control of agriculture and industry...

"The SWCC recognizes that even after the private capitalists are defeated, there is still a real danger of state capitalism, a system which under the guise of socialism really continues to protect the privileges a few against the needs of the many. Therefore the SWCC demands that every government organ be made subject to democratic worker control."

*Submitted to Prime Minister's Advisory Committee on Workers' Participation. From Workers' Time, vol. 1, no. 4, March 1976.

ity of the cooperatives to include the factories in
their movement weakened their political impact, and
solidified growing differences between factory and
farm workers. Factory workers received higher pay
than field laborers; on the other hand, the co-op
members had received severance pay while the factory
operatives had not. Unable to extend the cooperative
organization to the factories, the cooperators on the
cane farms lost potentially valuable allies in the
face of pressures from the staff and government
officials to limit their control.

The Cooperatives and the Government

The government influenced the cooperatives
through its hold over their money, through its allies
among the executive staff of the co-ops and through
the centralized structure of the cooperatives joined
at the top level into the United Sugar Workers Cooperative Council (USWCC).

All funds from cane sales had to be channelled
through the Sugar Industry Authority (SIA), which
decided what prices should be paid for sugar, how much
of the money should go to the cooperatives, and when
the proceeds would be sent out to them. The SIA
negotiated all the loans, and without its help, the
cooperatives could not obtain any credit.

Government influence over the cooperatives was
facilitated by the centralized organizational structure of the USWCC. The major business decisions at
the central level were made by the General Secretary.
By exerting their influence on the chief executive of
the USWCC, government officials wielded indirect
control over the cooperatives. Through his presence
at all of the Central Board meetings, the General
Secretary was in a position to influence the co-op
leadership on any vital decisions. The General
Secretary was the cooperatives' liaison with most of
the government agencies. The most influential of
these, besides the SIA, was the Ministry of Agriculture, whose Permanent Secretary in 1976, Desmond
Leakey, was also Chairman of the Frome Monymusk Land
Company.

The Central Board of the USWCC met monthly,
sometimes more often (1). Present at the meetings
were delegates from each of the three Estate Boards

who were the voting members, USWCC executives, several non-government advisors chosen by the Central Board and representatives from the government's Ministry of Agriculture, the Registrar of Cooperatives, and the SIA. During 1976 and 1977, one or two advisors from the Social Action Centre were usually present. By 1978, the government's opposition to their presence had succeeded; SAC advisors no longer attended Central Board meetings on a regular basis.

A Managing Committee member from one of the Frome farms recalls the unwillingness of Central Board members to take a strong, decisive stand on issues when confronted by USWCC executives, or by government officials or other "experts":

> When the men go to Central Board (meetings) their discussion is not that strong. When the Central Board members come back they cannot show you that "We go there and we fight". They are just weaklings in some of the meetings. (Cleaveland Dobson)

Because of the tradition of deference by workers to middle class professionals (who formed the advisory component), the financial dependence of the cooperatives on the government, and the lack of information and technical knowledge of its members, the USWCC Central Board often bowed to the expertise of its executives and the government advisors, and did not adequately defend the interests of the cooperators.

Crucial matters facing the Central Board such as staff demands for higher pay were usually referred to small subcommittees like the Finance Committee, whose membership almost always included a USWCC staff executive. This placed him in a position to control their deliberations through the information he provided (or failed to provide) and to shape decisions by arguments based on his knowledge and expertise.

The Central and Estate Boards also made many excellent decisions which were not, however, carried out by the executives. For example, the Central and Estate Boards decided several times that salaries of staff should be made public to be more closely monitored by the cooperators who were their employers, but this was never done. Nevertheless, the workers' committees did implement some progressive decisions, beginning with a reduction in the number of central level executives. Also, they had unprecedented access to the government during the PNP era. Sugar worker representatives were able to argue their case directly with top government officials, sometimes bringing large groups of workers with them to such meetings.

Prompted in part by its uneasiness about their autonomy, the PNP government attempted to reorganize the cooperatives in 1978. This move was also generated by the government's dismay over the cooperatives' continuing losses, and its need to secure a pending loan of U.S.$23 million from the World Bank to finance the modernization of the sugar factories on the three estates. A committee established by the government to explore organizational alternatives for the cooperatives was chaired by Michael Shaw, head of the Sugar Industry Research Institute. It proposed to abolish the Central Board and bring the operation of the three estates under direct government control.

The Shaw report recommended that the USWCC be retained as an organization with its functions limited to education, and that the Tractor and Transport and Irrigation Departments be placed under the jurisdiction of the National Sugar Company. The report also called for a moratorium on the cooperatives' debts, and greater autonomy for the estates to approach banks independently for loans. The government agreed to most of the proposals of the Shaw committee and planned to appoint commissioners to head each of the three estates. These three persons would have been directly responsible to the Ministry of Agriculture and would have had veto power over any Managing Committee decisions.

Although intense opposition was voiced at the Central Board meeting when the Shaw plan was presented (particularly by Monymusk representatives) and despite the threat the plan posed to the cooperatives' autonomy, the USWCC accepted the recommendations of the Shaw Commission. The plan, however, was never implemented because of continuing opposition from the Monymusk representatives, because the government could not locate qualified personnel for the commissioner positions, and because the proposal would have involved a massive refinancing of the cooperatives for which the government was unable to find the funds.

A major weapon the workers possessed in their battle with the government was the threat of strikes, which would interfere with the sugar factories' production and reduce the nation's foreign exchange income. The sugar workers went on strike a number of times for higher wages, for the payment of bonus and retroactive pay, and for the return of their severance money. They succeeded in encouraging the SIA to find revenue for various payments much more quickly than it otherwise would have done.

Paradoxically, the strikes also reflected the weakness of the cooperatives. If the workers really had control, they would not have had to strike. Many of the strikes were organized and coordinated by the JLP-affiliated BITU. For example, the January 1978 strike that involved all the cooperatives was called by Clifton Stone, Island Supervisor for the union, who visited all 23 farms personally. Such strikes served to affirm the workers' trade union ideology and to strengthen the hold of the unions over the cooperative members. Top union officials were allied with the government in that their leadership represented the same upper-middle-class interests. In fact, there was an interlocking movement of some union leaders to high government positions, and vice versa. The unions mirrored the bureaucratic side of the PNP vision which opposed real workers' autonomy that would undercut their own influence among the workers. Also, the strikes reinforced the idea that there existed an adversary relationship, although it was never clear to the workers exactly who was the adversary. Was it the government, the staff, the USWCC executives, or their own Managing Committees? The involvement of workers in union activities and their participation in union backed strikes weakened their allegiance to the cooperatives and made them feel that in spite of their formal ownership of the farms, little had really changed.

Severance Pay: A Hidden Time Bomb

The efforts of the Managing Committees to run the farms were hampered by the continuing controversy over the return of the workers' severance pay. The severance issue plagued the cooperatives from their inception to the very end, and in fact helped to hasten their demise. This issue was perhaps the biggest single cause of dissatisfaction among the membership, and the way it was handled served to discredit both the cooperative leadership and the PNP government. For these reasons the issue merits a more detailed look.

Severance pay, pro-rated according to length of employment, was due any workers who lost their job through no fault of their own. When WISCO sold its holdings to the Jamaican government, part of the negotiations included an agreement that the government would assume responsibility for payment of severance accumulated by the workers from the date they were first employed by WISCO. The cooperative members received severance pay because of a legal technicality which points out that the change to cooperatives meant the workers were losing their jobs by becoming self employed.

The severance pay issue was created by the government's unwillingness or inability to simply give the farm assets to the cooperatives; instead it sold them to the workers when they assumed the business. But the cooperatives had almost no equity capital. The funds used by the co-ops to purchase the standing cane and equipment from the government, therefore, came in part from loans contributed by the members themselves. This amounted to J$4.7 million which was half the severance pay owed to them collectively. (The total included some funds which had already been made available for the three pilot farms through loans from their members in 1974.) The government gave the cooperators the other half of the severance in cash. Those that did not want to join the co-ops received the full severance money. Many workers joined the cooperatives primarily to obtain the severance money while insuring their continued employment, rather than because they understood or believed in cooperative organization.

The seeds of recurrent controversy were sown by the ill-fated decision to finance the three pilot farms with loans from the workers. This was the outcome of early negotiations between the workers' leaders, their SAC advisors, and Land Company officials in 1974. The Land Company had encouraged the workers to invest their entire severance money. The workers were reluctant to part with any of their anticipated windfall. A compromise was reached whereby the workers lent half their severance pay to

104

the cooperatives for two years at 8 percent interest. Neither the Land Company officials, the workers' leaders, nor the SAC representatives insisted that the workers' investment be in the form of equity shares instead of loans. In retrospect this was a crucial mistake. Had the severance pay money which was used to finance the business been defined as shares instead of loans, the cooperatives could have commenced with a stronger financial foundation, and the members would not have been expecting the imminent return of these funds.

Because of the record high world sugar prices in 1975, the pilot farms were able to repay their loans from the members out of their profits. The precedent was unfortunate for the other farms that subsequently did not enjoy such favorable conditions. When the 17 "second wave" cooperatives began in 1976 and when the last three joined in 1977, they followed the pattern set by the pilot farms; their members agreed to lend half their severance pay to the co-ops for two years at 8 percent interest. Some of the younger members had only a few hundred dollars invested, while a number of those with more than 20 years' seniority had several thousand dollars invested in the business. The average was about J$1,000 per member (see Table 4.1). Buoyed by the optimism generated by high sugar prices and the profits made the first year by the pilot farms, the remaining cooperatives looked forward to future surplus that would be used to repay the members' loans. In their enthusiasm, co-op organizers may have overemphasized the profitability of the sugar business and did not educate members thoroughly on the cyclical nature of sugar prices and the fact that they were taking over an ailing industry.

Most of the cane farms on the three estates had suffered financial losses under corporate and government management and could not fully recover under severely handicapped cooperative control. The co-ops began with almost no equity and an enormous debt of about J$10 million. The workers' J$4.7 million investment was considered as a <u>loan</u>, the interest on which amounted to J$1.9 million over a five-year period. The cooperatives were scarcely able to pay this interest, let alone return the principal.

Worker unrest over the severance money was a continuing irritant and source of instability. The

TABLE 4.1: MEMBER SEVERANCE DEPOSITS, BY SEX, AT TWO FROME FARMS, 1980

Severance Money Invested in Co-op	SHREWSBURY				ALBANY			
	Number		Percent		Number		Percent	
	W	M	W	M	W	M	W	M
$3000 or more	0	3	0	2	4	21	6	15
2500–2999	0	6	0	4	6	14	10	11
2000–2999	2	15	5	10	7	14	12	11
1500–1999	5	33	12	23	13	16	22	12
1000–1499	13	40	32	28	9	19	15	14
500–999	16	29	39	20	10	26	17	20
400 or less	5	18	12	13	11	23	18	17
TOTAL	41	144	100	100	60	133	100	100

SOURCE: Estate records

106

severance issue was a built-in time bomb which exploded when the payments were due in 1978 and then once more in 1981. In January 1978, the workers began clamoring for the return of their severance. They stopped work for several weeks to voice their demand for the money. The government and the unions worked out a postponement of this crisis under a compromise. A loan plan was negotiated by government officials and representatives of the National Commercial Bank. The government made arrangements with the bank which enabled co-op members to apply for bank loans which used as collateral the money they originally lent to the co-ops (half their severance pay, which continued to be on loan to the co-ops). Each member could borrow from the bank up to two-thirds of the amount they had invested in the cooperative. Payments on these bank loans were to be made through payroll deductions while co-op members continued to wait for the cooperatives to return their severance money. This loan plan was presented to leaders from both major unions by the Minister of Agriculture, A. U. Belinfanti, in January 1978.

The government did not find it necessary to include any workers or their co-op representatives in these discussions. Through this temporary solution imposed by the government, the cooperative leaders were forced to promise their members the return of the severance money at the end of another three years, even though the government was well aware that the gap between the cost of production and what it was paying for cane would cause the co-ops to have even greater deficits during that time, making it even more difficult for them to repay the money they had borrowed from their members.

In 1981, the loans again came due, and again the workers demanded the return of their severance money. The cooperative leaders tried to obtain a government commitment to at least repay the J$900,000 in severance due to the oldest members in 1980-81. This would have allowed several hundred members over age 65 to retire while simultaneously cutting the cooperatives' labor costs. But even this compromise was never implemented. The long wait for the return of the severance money coupled with what the workers saw as a string of broken promises destroyed the workers' morale and caused them to lose faith in their leaders

and in the cooperative organization. As one of the
Frome workers put it:

> What caused the co-op to be wrecked was
> just because the people didn't get
> their severance pay. And you could
> preach like Paul and sing like angels--
> there was nothing you could say to them
> to get their hearts settled because
> their intention was the money. When we
> go out there, they say, "We want the
> money." Every time they hear (co-op
> leaders) say they don't have the money,
> the money is in the cane root. That's
> what caused the co-op to go down.
> (Clara Belle Gayle)

The Managing Committees appeared ineffective to their
members because they could not obtain any satisfactory
resolution of the severance issue. The PNP government
never came up with the necessary funds. The JLP
government subsequently "found" the necessary money to
repay all the severance, but only at the price of
taking back the cane farms from the workers.

Why Didn't the Government
Give More Help to the Co-ops?

The government never gave the cooperatives enough
assistance to enable them to become economically
viable, in spite of the fact that Prime Minister
Manley himself mentioned the sugar workers' cooperatives as an illustration of how the government was
implementing democratic socialism. Why then didn't
the PNP government provide more help to the one
large-scale example of workers' cooperatives actually
established in Jamaica, and why did it oppose almost
every effort by the USWCC to maintain or increase its
autonomy?

One reason was the country's desperate economic
situation. The government was hemmed in by its
chronic shortage of foreign exchange and its continued
economic dependence on foreign financial institutions
and governments. The sugar industry, of which the
cooperatives were a vital part, was seen as a means of
obtaining government revenue. The government resisted
the cooperatives' fight for independence because it
was afraid this might interfere with the cane supply

108

and endanger some of the much-needed foreign exchange derived from sugar.

Further, throughout the PNP's tenure in office between 1972 and 1980, there was an internal power struggle between its center/right and left-wing factions, with Manley trying to steer a precarious course between them. Leftist leaders Hugh Small and D.K. Duncan supported the cooperatives. Some government officials, such as the Ministry of Agriculture advisor to the Central Board, Mrs. Una Saunders, were quite favorable toward the co-ops, but such persons had only a limited influence within the party.

From the very beginning, the PNP center/right-wing factions fought against the mobilization efforts of SAC and the SWCC. These organizations were opposed by cabinet officials within the PNP such as Minister of Agriculture A.U. Belinfanti, and by advisors such as Richard Fletcher (Manley's brother-in-law and at one time Chairman of the SIA). A paper presented to the PNP Executive Committee late in 1975 depicted the SWCC as a political liability, making the party more vulnerable to attacks by the opposition JLP. The paper discussed ways to split the SWCC leadership from the cooperative movement on the sugar farms, and boasted that "McCulloch has single-handedly destroyed SWCC credibility on at least six farms."(2)

An illustration of the continuing conflict between left and center/right factions within the PNP is found in the internal debate over whether or not to turn to the International Monetary Fund (IMF) to help the country through its foreign exchange crisis (3). After months of indecision, in 1977 Manley finally decided to seek loans from the IMF to cope with the massive government deficit, and from the World Bank to rehabilitate the sugar factories at Frome, Monymusk and Bernard Lodge. Predictably, one of the conditions imposed by the IMF was that the government refrain from further subsidies to the sugar workers' cooperatives. The World Bank was also negative toward the co-ops. A World Bank report made in connection with the government's loan application acknowledges the need to replace cultivation, loading and transport machinery on the three estates. The report states, however, that "until the serious deficiencies of the cooperatives are corrected...there can be no assurances that the portion of such equipment which might be made available to the cooperatives would be put to good use. Consequently, the proposed project specifically excludes any capital improvements for the cane farmers." (4)

Most of the time it was in office, the PNP and the government bureaucracy were dominated by center-right factions representing the small upper-middle-class, who were unwilling to relinquish their control to more militant party members, much less to uneducated workers and small farmers. The ideology of democratic socialism was used to woo voters, but the dominant factions within the party lacked the desire to put it into practice. Thus, the PNP was incapable of carrying out a socialist transformation of the economy and the state apparatus; it never provided enough resources to the cooperatives for them to become viable, and it resisted the efforts of the Managing Committees to translate their formal authority over the staff into actual control of the sugar estates.

The Bushas' Opposition to Workers' Control

The farm staff never liked the cooperative idea and tried to prevent the birth of the co-ops. Although they failed in this, they continued their opposition. The sugar workers' leadership was involved in continuous battles with the staff on the central, estate and farm levels. In some ways, this was an extension of the cooperatives' struggles with the government. Under the hierarchical structure carried over from former days, staff policies were handed down to the estates from USWCC headquarters, and estate executives transmitted orders down to the farm managers. The government was thus able to use its influence over the executive staff at the central level to reach down into the estates and the farms.

The lengths to which the staff went in their efforts to sabotage the workers' leadership is illustrated by two incidents. The first was the "bogus chairmen" episode that occurred at Frome just prior to the start of the main group of cooperatives there. Prime Minister Manley, touring the country before the 1976 elections, went to Frome to have a first-hand look at how the people felt about the proposed cooperatives. He scheduled a public meeting to be followed by discussions with the Chairmen of the Managing

Committees. Some of the staff arranged for Manley to meet with a set of fake "chairmen" (who were workers loyal to the bushas)in a maneuver that almost succeeded. The Frome staff kept the real Managing Committee chairmen in ignorance of the time and place of the meeting. Word about the staff plans leaked out, and the real Chairmen rushed to the Staff Club where they interrupted the masquerade. Matthias Brown, at that time an SWCC organizer, describes the scene:

> We reached (the Staff Club) in time to see eleven "chairmen" lined up with all the dignitaries of the Frome Monymusk Land Company who were to introduce the imposter chairmen to the Prime Minister. Only two of the authentic Chairmen from the Steering Committee were there. The rest were imposters. (The "chairmen") they (the staff) had manipulated and brought there would not speak to the Prime Minister; the bushas and dignitaries from the Frome Monymusk Land Company would do the talking. The fake chairmen were busha people, when the busha would go out there and say what the people want, they would say "yes" and keep silent.

A second incident occurred just as the "second wave" cooperatives were about to begin. In 1976, co-op leaders decided that cane reaping would not start until the government acceded to their demand that the Ministry of Agriculture provide a document validating the cooperatives' control of the land. Managers at Frome, however, tried to start the harvest in defiance of this Estate and Central Board decision. The Chairpersons of some of the farm Managing Committees went out and stood in the fields to prevent the cane burning which would have made harvest mandatory. Their action forced Parliamentary Secretary for Agriculture Desmond Leakey to fly to Frome to hold talks with the workers' leaders. Subsequently, Leakey met with the Central Board, which made him agree to provide the cooperatives with an interim "letter of possession" in lieu of the leases which were not yet ready (5).

111

The Implementation of Workers' Control, 1976-1978

The high point of worker control was attained during the year after the victory of the PNP in the 1976 elections. The Managing Committees made the staff more accountable, and undercut their ability to withhold work from the members. Recalling the early days of the cooperative, one of the members at Frome comments:

> The Project Managers would have to come when the (Managing) Committee had their discussion. All of them had to come together and say "All right, this must be done this week," and so on. They didn't like it, because previously they used to have their way to do their business by themselves.
> (Clara Belle Gayle)

A major power of the sugar workers' Estate and Central Boards lay in their ability to hire and fire the top executives. The Central Board eliminated several executive positions and drastically reduced the central office budget in 1976. On the estate level, the Frome Board fired one of the executives, Jasper Bucknor, whom it held responsible for the fake chairmen episode. At Monymusk, the Board forced chief executive Archie Savariau to resign in 1978 after he flagrantly ignored their instructions.

The Estate and Central Boards repeatedly discussed reducing the field staff from four to three positions on each farm, but never took action on this because of unified staff opposition. Overall, they reduced the number of employees from about 310 in 1975 to 258 by 1980 (6). Most of this was accomplished by attrition. Also, reduction of staff was implemented by declaring redundant certain positions inherited from the Land Company. Finally, staff reduction resulted from the Managing Committees' attempts to clean up the mismanagement and corruption that had been endemic under WISCO and the Land Company. During the cooperatives' six year history, at least two dozen employees were fired for payroll padding, theft of funds, or similar offenses, and some of them were not replaced.

112

The struggle between the Managing Committees and staff was especially fierce at the farm level, where the Project Managers (the former bushas) had been accustomed to exercising undisputed authority and where the Assistant Project Managers and Bookkeepers felt most threatened by worker control. The Managing Committees challenged the staff on the allocation of work, the awarding of premium time, and workers' promotions. Staff resisted the Managing Committees by overt opposition, withholding information, forming alliances with key committee members, and sabotage. The employees coordinated their efforts through their Staff Associations (eventually affiliated with the Union of Technical, Administrative, and Supervisory Personnel) which engaged in collective bargaining on their behalf.

The workers' committees were able to successfully appeal to cooperative principles, and used cooperative ideology to further their efforts. They also had the weapon of publicity whereby they could expose actions the staff would have preferred to keep secret. The progressive leadership was aided by <u>Workers Time</u>, published monthly by the Social Action Centre and distributed free on the farms. This publication always included a centerfold with pictures or drawings explaining cooperative issues designed to be understood even by illiterate sugar workers. The farm Managing Committees also had the authority to hire and fire staff (at least until 1978). When the cooperatives began, a few of the most objectionable bushas were rejected by farm members' votes and had to be replaced. In theory, the Managing Committees could require their managers to submit information and timely reports, and to review and revise budgets, although their inexperience resulted in rare exercise of these powers.

The Managing Committees were hampered in their effectiveness in that their members did not have sufficient training in such skills as analyzing budgets and were systematically deprived of the information they needed to make intelligent decisions. They had inadequate data about their own employees. The committees never obtained the lists of individual staff salaries they requested, nor did they have copies of written job descriptions against which they could measure the performance of their employees. Further, the managers resisted the implementation of

113

budget control systems so that the farms, estates, and service units continued to overspend while the Managing Committees were kept unaware of the full extent of the deficits until it was too late for corrective action. No effective cost control was implemented by the cooperatives until the organization development program coordinated by SAC at Monymusk and Bernard Lodge between 1979 and 1981.

The workers' leadership was disadvantaged in exerting effective control over the staff because of the unequal access to resources. The staff had access to the jeeps, phones, radios, office records, and the keys to the buildings and storerooms. They had a monopoly of information and of such skills as making up payrolls. In addition, the Project Managers attended Managing Committee meetings as ex-officio members, but no workers were present at staff meetings. Even when the Managing Committees did hold private caucuses, one or two members friendly to the staff would often carry inside information back to them. The staff knew the workers' plans but were able to keep their own plans secret.

The Return of the Busha

The Managing Committees were unable to turn their formal authority over the staff into a decisive edge, and eventually the staff was able to regain many of the powers that the Managing Committees had claimed. The reasons for this included the cooperatives' constant economic crises and their continuing dependence on government agencies that controlled their purse strings, their dependence on the staff for information and expertise, the timidity, and lack of experience of committee members, and the absence of any effective education program during the early years. In addition, the skillful maneuvering by staff weakened the Managing Committees' credibility with co-op members, and assigned the blame for unpopular decisions such as enforcing discipline to them.

The co-op leaders came to be viewed unfavorably by the members because they often were the bearers of bad news; always the leaders came back from Kingston saying: "There is no money," or "We don't know when the money will be paid." They would plead with the members to continue working, "A strike is a strike against yourselves. You are the owners." Yet, when the members in their frustration would strike or demonstrate, soon thereafter staff members would come to them with the "good news" that the money would be paid on a certain date. The Project Managers would be notified by the executive staff in Kingston and usually knew when such payments would be made before the co-op leaders found out or had the time to inform the membership. To many members, it confirmed what they suspected: that the co-op was not really theirs but the staff's. It appeared to some that their own leaders couldn't -- or didn't want to -- help their own people as they were supposed to.

The reassertion of staff influence over the farms paralleled the waning of the Social Action Centre's presence. After the initial organizing period, SAC drew back from the cooperatives. This reflected the SAC ideology that the workers should run the organization on their own as soon as possible. Also, it was the result of strong opposition to SAC by key government officials, including Minister of Agriculture Belinfanti and the Director of the Cooperative Development Centre, Cedric McCulloch, by the leadership of both major national unions, and by farm staff who spread contradictory rumors and innuendoes that SAC was "communist" or working for the American CIA. The managers were more than willing to step into the vacuum created by the SAC retreat. Other than a few Member Service Officers on each estate (and later, during 1980 and 1981, several education staff) there was no progressive pro-cooperative cadre to help the workers' committees.

At the expiration of their original 22-month guaranteed employment with the Land Company which had maintained them on behalf of the co-ops, the staff won a very favorable contract for renewed employment with the USWCC. The contract was drafted by a joint committee of Staff Association and USWCC Central Board representatives. Some of its key provisions were published in the May 1977 issue of Workers Time (7). Revisions were made by a committee that included General Secretary Higgins and several government advisors (8).

The contract was discussed by the Central Board and adopted almost without opposition. It was never taken before the cooperative membership for approval or rejection. The members were distracted at this

115

time by the burning issue of the return of the severance monies due in January 1978 and they paid little
attention to the staff contract. Thus the membership
was not fully aware of its contents until after it
went into effect at the end of January 1978. The new
contract guaranteed the staff lifetime tenure and
removed the power to hire and fire staff from the farm
Managing Committees. Henceforth, they were to be
employed and discharged by the Central Board of the
USWCC at the recommendation of the Chief Executive
Officers of the three estates.

The very wording of the contract is indicative of
how successful the employees had been in consolidating
their positions: "Staff members will not be directed,
persuaded, instructed, coerced, influenced, or threatened to act in any manner contrary to the direction of
the Estate Chief Executive Officer in conduct or in
managerial matters by members of the cooperatives,
their Committee members or Chairmen." Further, staff
were not required to become members of the cooperatives. They were granted additional fringe benefits,
including generous vacations, sick leave, automobile
loans, and pensions. After the new contract was
adopted, the staff continued to push aggressively for
a continuation of their disproportionate share of the
material benefits. There were at least three staff
strikes. During one of the strikes at Monymusk in
1978, employees hid the members' pay slips. Undaunt-
ed, some of the workers assumed the administrative
duties while the staff were on strike; the members
received their pay as usual. Subsequently, the
Monymusk Estate Board decided to institute a program
to comprehensively train members how to make up
payrolls so as to deprive the staff of their monopoly
of knowledge in this area.

The last staff strike during the co-op era took
place in May 1981. It was obvious by this time that
the members were quite capable of running the cultivation and reaping operations by themselves. Field work
continued virtually uninterrupted during the two-week
strike. Even the payroll was handled mostly by the
cooperators, although at Frome help from the education
staff was needed on some of the farms. Two cooperators at Frome who had been promoted to positions as
accounting clerks, but who also remained members of
the cooperatives, were crucial in helping the other
farms complete their payroll on time. The staff

116

sensed the members' ability to run the farms without them as a threat to their jobs, and they terminated the strike and returned to work.

Internal Conflicts Within the Cooperatives

The Managing Committees not only faced conflicts with the government and staff, but they had to contend with conflicts within the cooperatives as well. These conflicts included the resentment by the members of special privileges enjoyed by the Managing Committees, as well as the attempts of some of the farms to maintain their autonomy from the cooperatives' Estate and Central Boards.

The membership of the Managing Committees was drawn disproportionately from the more educated workers and from those who were supervisors. There was a tendency for Managing Committee members to develop into a stratum of more privileged workers with easier jobs, freedom to travel, modest expense accounts, and (for a few) access to vehicles. Many of the same persons continued to serve on the Central and Estate Boards year after year (9).

Some of the Managing Committee members were already supervisors when they were first elected; others were more likely to be promoted to supervisors, because of their membership in the committees. Chairpersons generally did only "chairpersons' work" (which did not involve field labor) with the tacit approval of the committees and the staff. Further, there were noticeable pay differences between the upper stratum of the work force and the ordinary sugar workers. Chairpersons at Monymusk were averaging J$5,778 gross annual income in 1977, more than three times the income of the cultivation workers (10). Income for supervisors was about double that of the rank and file laborers, partly because the supervisors worked the whole year round (11). We did not find disproportionate pay increases for supervisors and chairpersons at Frome.

Although most of the workers' leadership was extremely dedicated, some Managing Committee members used their positions for personal advancement. There were even a few who enriched themselves by fraud or theft. One such incident led to the dismissal of the first Vice President of the Central Board, a represen-

117

tative from Frome. At Monymusk, two Chairpersons and a Managing Committee Secretary were expelled for fraud or corruption (12). Also, there were opportunist leaders who allied themselves with the staff and formed a continuing source of internal friction.

The rank and file members perceived the Managing Committees with ambivalence; they were regarded as champions of the workers' cause, but also as another power group that would pursue its own interests. The workers' resentment of the Managing Committees' evolution into more privileged groups led to protests. In April 1977, militant workers at Frome's Georges Plain led a strike sparked by the issue of special privileges for committee members and staff. The walkout was joined by workers from Frome farm and Blue Castle.

A four hour meeting was held at Georges Plain, chaired by Uriel Burley, a cane cutter who was not a Managing Committee member. The workers demanded that the Estate Board meet to discuss a number of concerns:

- The Estate Board should not continue to make decisions without the full knowledge of the workers.

- Information regarding the staff salaries must be presented to the workers and discussed openly.

- An emergency loan fund should be set up for the workers.

- Severance pay due in January must be returned.

- All staff and supervisors must do one day's work per week in the fields.

- Board members must do their committee work on a voluntary basis, and their wages must be approved by the members. They must do their regular jobs except when they have to attend meetings (13).

In response, the Estate Board promised to publish a monthly bulletin and publicize information on staff salaries which were to be obtained from the Chief Executive. The Cooperative Department said it would

118

help the workers establish a revolving loan fund.
Although the salary data were never forwarded, a loan
fund was set up and was one of the lasting gains from
the protest. Staff, supervisors, and Managing Committee Chairpersons promised to join the workers in the
fields, and some of them actually worked there for a
few hours the next day. Workers Time carried a
picture of Georges Plain Chairman Gladstone Thomas and
Frome Chief Executive E.B. Thompson spreading fertilizer with a gang of field workers. This was a
significant symbolic act in that this task was considered a lowly one and had always been relegated to the
women, but the gesture was never repeated. The Staff
Association subsequently disavowed any agreement and
said it would never consent to staff working in the
fields.

The cooperatives were also beset by disputes over
the issue of centralization vs. local control. One of
the purposes of the three-tier structure of primary
farms, estates, and the central USWCC was to insure
the strength and unity of the movement. The USWCC's
three level structure, inherited from the Land Company, was continued because it would retain one voice
which represented all 5,000 members. The organizers
believed that one large group would be more successful
in dealing with the government and the banks than many
smaller ones. Centralization was also seen as a
useful means of standardizing the relationships
between the cooperatives and outside contractors, and
of saving money through bulk purchases for all the
farms. The centralized structure did allow the USWCC
to act as a forceful lobby on behalf of the sugar
workers with the government. Its disadvantages were
that it severely limited the degree of local control
on the farms and that it facilitated domination of the
cooperatives by the estate and central level executives, and through them, by the government.

At the primary co-op level, the Managing Committees were never fully in charge of their farms. Not
only was the staff constantly trying to reassert its
authority, but many business decisions were pre-empted
by the Estate and Central Boards. A committee member
from one of the Monymusk farms complains:

The Monymusk Estate Board shouldn't
have so much control over the farm.
Give us our (own) tractors. It would

119

be better. Everything you want to do,
the Estate (Board) says you can't do
it. You could know how to cut your
budget if you did control your own
business. But everything has to go to
the (Estate) Board, and they make
decisions there. (Norma Brown)

The issue of local autonomy usually came up when
one of the farms had some unanticipated income it
wanted to keep for itself, or saw an opportunity to
cut costs by proceeding independently. For example,
in 1977 the Frome Estate Board decided to lease a
quarry at the Georges Plain farm to a private contractor. The Georges Plain members opposed this because
they wanted to mine it themselves. The dispute ended
in an agreement in which the farm members were to
operate the quarry and pay a royalty to the estate.

At Bernard Lodge, the Estate Board itself voiced
demands for independence from the USWCC. Part of the
issue was that the farms on the Bernard Lodge estate
were among the most cost efficient. If they could
save the money the USWCC charged them for central
office services some of the farms might make a profit.
It was also felt that the estate would do better in
negotiating for bank loans if it could be independent
of debt-ridden Monymusk by disassociating from the
USWCC.

The struggle for autonomy was strongest within
the three pilot farms, Barham, Morelands and Salt
Pond. Each of these farms had already formed their
own identity for a year before the other cooperatives
joined them and before the Estate and Central Boards
were established. The Managing Committees on these
three farms were protective of their powers and
reluctant to share them with other workers' committees. They resisted joining the estate and central
cooperatives. (Salt Pond farm at Bernard Lodge
maintained its independence throughout the cooperative
era.) The reason the pilot farms wanted autonomy was
based on the ideology of democracy and local control,
as well as on the fact that tying the more productive
cane farms to an estate and central structure increased their overhead greatly. Their potential profit was
drawn away into unnecessarily high payments made to
cover the cost of inefficient Tractor and Transport
service branches, while their payments for the estate

and USWCC staff subsidized the salaries and benefits of those who seemed to contribute little to the direct productivity of the cane farms (14).

Frome's Barham Managing Committee was proud of their farm's record of earning a profit in both its first and second years. The Barham members' severance deposits had been returned to them, and a separate farm bank account was established to keep the profits. With these funds, the farm managed to purchase some of its own tractors.

Barham's Managing Committee adopted a 10-point program in 1979; its main features were: that income from cane sales should be lodged in Barham's own bank account instead of being kept by the SIA or the USWCC; that the contract for hauling cane previously provided by the Land Company and then by the estate be taken from the T&T unit and shifted to a private contractor; that fertilizer and herbicide be stored directly on the farm so that Barham would have control over its own supplies; and that insurance funds for deceased members be administered directly by the farm instead of by the estate or central offices.

The decision to replace the Tractor and Transport services with those of a private contractor enabled Barham to cut some of its costs. The Frome Estate Board objected to Barham hiring tractor services from outside because this meant that the burden of the T&T overhead would have to be borne by the remaining farms. The Board decided that Barham must use the T&T services after all, and that it must remain a member of the secondary and tertiary level organizations. When the farm refused to comply, the Board took the matter to court and won. Barham resumed purchasing its hauling services from T&T and joined the USWCC.

The power struggles between the workers' committees and the government and staff, and the attempts by local committees to assert control over their farms, were paralleled by an ideological battle, much of which centered around the implementation of an education program that would help the workers to break free of the old plantation mentality and to adopt a new cooperative ideology.

1. The distance separating the three estates made it difficult to hold Central Board meetings more frequently. Members from Frome had to travel about 135 miles to the USWCC offices in Kingston where the meetings were held, a trip that usually took no less than 3 1/2 hours each way.

2. We are indebted to Carl Feuer for sending us a copy of this document.

3. A PNP conference in September 1977 solidified the hold of the center/right factions on the party. This was symbolized by the resignation of the outspoken left-wing Minister of Mobilization, D. K. Duncan, soon after the conference.

4. World Bank, Staff Appraisal Report, Sugar Rehabilitation Project, Jamaica, January 19, 1978.

5. The leases were delayed because the books of the Frome Monymusk Land Company were in such disorder it could not justify the price it was asking the co-ops to pay for the cane that was standing in the fields.

6. Two new categories of added staff are included in the latter figures: the 11 Member Service Officers hired in 1976, and the 15 teachers who were recruited in 1979 to implement the IAF-funded education program. Most of the Member Service Officers and education staff played an important role as allies of the progressive leadership of the Managing Committees.

7. Central Board minutes, April 5, 1977.

8. Central Board minutes, May 3, 1977.

9. The cooperatives never limited the number of terms in office for members or officers of the Managing Committees.

10. Carl Feuer, Jamaica and Sugar Worker Cooperatives: The Politics of Reform (Ph.D. Diss., Cornell University, 1983), p. 325.

11. According to Feuer, supervisors at Springfield were paid an average of J$3,070 in 1975, while laborers received J$1,690. By 1977, the figures

were J$3,663 and J$1,560 respectively. At Morelands, the pilot farm at Monymusk, supervisors received J$3,897 in 1975, laborers J$2,016. In 1977, the former were receiving J$4,015 while the latter got J$2,122. _Ibid_. table 10.5, p. 322.

12. _Ibid._, p. 291.

13. _Workers Time_ 2:3&4, April-May, 1977.

14. The high cost of hauling and transport was discussed by the Central and Estate Boards many times over the years, but no action was ever taken. The Central Board discussed the situation in 1976, when it was pointed out that it was cheaper to employ contractors to do the work than to have T&T units do it. The matter was referred to the Estate Boards but never resolved. The Monymusk Board tried for years to rid itself of its T&T unit, and have it put under the jurisdiction of the National Sugar Company, so that the co-ops would not be burdened by its losses, but both the government and the T&T members resisted this.

At Frome, one-fourth of the _total_ outlay of the farms went to pay for the Tractor and Transport unit, which was then only hauling cane for 6 or 7 of the 10 farms. This was in fact a hidden subsidy.

CHAPTER V

COOPERATIVE IDEOLOGY: THE SEARCH FOR UNITY

> It is a part of our tradition in Jamaica to compete against each other and that caused people to be a little bit selfish. But our duty was to change that selfishness to bring out more togetherness.
>
> There was a lot of political infighting over who should control cooperative education. Because one of the key things was education; who should control the minds of the people; whether the people's minds should be controlled by themselves and the co-op or by outside forces. (Matthias Brown)

The main objective of the worker leaders and the organizers in organizing the cooperatives was to institute worker ownership and control over the three sugar estates. To do this they had to fight a battle not only against external opposition, but they also struggled with the members themselves on many ideological fronts. Years of oppression had rooted in their minds a plantation mentality: the acceptance of class hierarchy and the superiority of experts and religiously inspired fatalism. What made this struggle all the more difficult for all those who supported the cooperative movement was the fact that on one hand the government had conceded to the movement relatively easily and quickly, but on the other hand it was not willing to turn full control of the cooperatives over to the workers. The civil service bureaucrats and the estate managers, as we have seen, retained considerable control over the cooperatives and they were in a position to obstruct or delay any education effort aimed at heightening the political consciousness of the workers and increasing real worker control. In their view worker education was acceptable only if they could control its content. To the farm staff, any form of worker education was perceived as a threat, since even purely technical expertise or mere literacy would increase the amount of input that the members could have in the decision-making process on the farms. The opponents of workers' control over the cooperatives skillfully exploited plantation ideology

and political party affiliations in order to sow
dissension among the members, to turn the members
against their own leaders and to encourage them to
destroy the cooperatives through their lack of support
or by sabotaging production. In their battle to
organize and preserve the cooperatives, the supporters
utilized elements of the same ideologies of plantation
and party, as well as cooperative philosophy, to
convince the members that true worker control was
possible and that cooperatives controlled by them
would bring real improvements in their lives.

Educating the workers for cooperative management
was all the more difficult because of the speed with
which the cooperatives were formed. One of the
organizers put it this way:

> We had anticipated a lot more opposi-
> tion from the government. I was taken
> by surprise at how easily they went
> along with the whole idea of coopera-
> tives. But I would have welcomed a lot
> more opposition. In a sense, it almost
> went through too easily. The necessary
> mettle that should have developed, that
> would have developed after a long
> struggle, simply didn't develop.
> Imagine, I started organizing in 1973
> and by the end of 1975 all the coopera-
> tives were on stream. That's three
> short years. What can you really hope
> to do in three short years?
> (Joe Owens)

The ideologies of the opponents and the supporters of the co-ops reflected the different class
positions they held in Jamaican society. To the
opponents (the staff and the bureaucrats) the sugar
workers were simply a lower order of human beings too
ignorant to become anything but manual laborers. They
felt contempt for the workers and feared that if they
associated themselves too closely with workers they
would lower their own status. Or, the workers were
seen paternalistically as children who needed to be
told what to do and be guided by them. The opponents
believed that the old hierarchical order, with them as
the experts in control, was the most efficient way of
managing the estates. But there was also a fear of
the workers who, in Carl Stone's words,

125

...seek to compensate for low levels of information and understanding by extreme militance and aggressive behavior in situations of conflict and disagreement. In this context, the common feeling among workers as being an underclass hardly accorded recognition as human beings and looked upon with scorn, fuels intense levels of class militancy (1).

The supporters (the organizers, co-op leaders and supportive members) viewed the workers as quite capable and intelligent human beings who, with technical and political education and access to power, could run the business. In their view, the limitations of the workers were predominantly the effect of an autocratic plantation hierarchy which for centuries had stifled the development of talent among the workers. The supporters were willing to undertake the struggle for worker control, convinced that the obstacles could be overcome and that the business could only be efficiently managed when all the members were satisfied mentally and materially. One of the main obstacles, but also a major source of strength, for the co-op leaders and organizers was what they called the "plantation mentality" and its hold over the members' minds.

The Plantation Mentality

As was pointed out earlier, the objective conditions of the sugar workers on the plantations had changed only minimally since the days of slavery. This fact was reflected on the ideological level in the tenacity of the plantation mentality. The main ingredients of this ideology were competition among the workers, selfishness and individualism, deference to authority and acceptance (although mixed with resentment) of outsiders as legitimate holders of authority, coupled with a distrust and envy of their own co-workers and a lack of confidence in their own ability and talent. However, it also included a strong identity as workers and producers, anger at the corrupt nature of the system and a willingness to take collective action, particularly when the rewards of that action were perceived as immediate and material in nature.

126

The differential rewards in the system led people to compete against each other and to see their own worth and that of the other workers in terms of an occupational hierarchy so that:

> The cane cutter would have thought himself better than the person who weeds the grass. The person who earns more as a cane cutter would think himself better than the one who earns less. The woman who is the driver (supervisor) would have thought herself better than the person who is fertilizing the field. (Matthias Brown)

But in the larger society they all shared the lack of prestige and low monetary value placed on their work.

The system made people fight each other and distrust each other because the busha would use workers and pit them against each other in order to secure his own position of power among them. In the past, he may have used a slave to give a lash to another, now he would use a worker to carry information to him about other workers. People knew that their poverty and powerlessness would make them specifically vulnerable to this kind of manipulation, and it created a deep fear in them, the fear of losing their livelihood.

> You know, they just have that fear in them, fear of expressing themselves to the staff. They, in the old days, in WISCO days, feared the staff. You know busha loves you, if you will carry a little news to him to keep on getting a bread, while this one don't do it and he's not counted.

> At all times you had to be submitting, you had to humble yourself to them, regardless of what they may do to you that is against your spirit. You just have to cope with it, so as to keep in line, so that you can get a livelihood. (Beryl Davis)

In addition to generating fear, poverty, powerlessness, and divisions among the workers, the plantation hierarchy also stripped them of their dignity, confidence and sense of self-worth.

> The bushas would not count you with
> them as a human. They would treat you
> like you were subhuman. You had to be
> running behind busha begging him for
> work; he would ride around on his horse
> and pay you no mind, until he feels
> like stopping. (Alexander James)

When the idea of the cooperative was being introduced to the workers in 1973-75, the majority simply could not believe that the government would let them have the business and that they could actually control and run it. Many had worked in the fields for 30 or 40 years and had always been told what to do. They did not believe that they could learn to manage a multi-million dollar business. This mentality, compounded by the relatively high average age (55 years) of the members, their illiteracy, and the defeatist feeling that they were simply too old to learn continued to hamper the education efforts. The doubts about the government allowing them to control the farms were also based on a good dose of realism, which as it turned out, was well-founded.

The old system stifled initiative, productivity, and the full development of each individual worker. However, it also produced a more positive ideology. It created in the workers a sense of themselves as producers and through that a feeling of strength.

> The staff don't do anything. They only
> inform and instruct us. We are doing
> the work. Not even the supervisors do
> anything. They only give orders. We
> the cooperators are doing the work.
> For instance, they come and say, take
> up this stake and if a cooperator does
> not take up the stake, it is not being
> taken up by them. Who does the work?
> (Woman Cooperator)

Among the women, particularly at Frome where women constituted about one-quarter of the work force, the feeling of being absolutely critical to the success of the business was very strongly developed. The women did most of the cultivation work and some of the

128

reaping; they generally agreed that, as one of them put it,

> Women take more interest in the work, more than the men. The men say they are not getting enough money and things like that, so they just feel frustrated, and they don't want to work. The majority of the work that's being carried out on the farm is by the women, especially this time of the year (summer). The women do the agricultural part, women have to cut the dribble (seed cane), women have to clean the cane, because the women have to fertilize the cane, women have to cut the seed for planting and what the machine can't cover, women have to go and recover. So you see, women do the most part. (Beryl Davis)

The system also created within them acute awareness of oppression and exploitation. The workers knew that only a small portion of their labor's value was returned to them. They saw that others benefited disproportionately from their work; their poverty stood in stark contrast to the well-being of their superiors. And, in spite of its divisiveness, the system did create a feeling of togetherness in being collectively on the bottom of the social hierarchy. "We as small people against them, the big men," the workers would say.

After 1938, this shared feeling of exploitation was transformed into organized power in the trade unions; the workers knew that collective action in the form of a strike could be used to extract more money from the company. This type of militancy was particularly well developed among the resident workers at Monymusk and Bernard Lodge where the majority were totally dependent upon estate labor for their livelihood, while most of the workers at Frome had small farm plots or other small business. For those at Frome more individually owned land would have been the ideal solution, although they were not strangers to cooperation; cooperation was practiced in buying and savings clubs, in helping a neighbor prepare his or her fields and in moving a house to a new site. Their somewhat wider range of economic activity had the

129

effect of decreasing their sense of vested interest in the estate. Nonetheless, they also had many features of a proletariat. Their work conditions subjected them to the uncertainties and oppression found on all sugar estates in Jamaica.

At one extreme the estate system produced individuals who came to love the busha, the source of rewards, favors, and power. They learned not to love or trust their own co-workers. They were individuals with little or no sense of sister- or brotherhood. At the other extreme the system created opposition in those workers who refused to accept the legitimacy of the plantation hierarchy and rebelled against it. They were often the ones who possessed resources such as literacy and some education, or a supervisory position, and who most keenly felt the injustice and disrespect accorded them by the white and light-skinned (brown) owners and managers. They were among the first to grasp at the opportunity to form a cooperative. One such individual was Matthias Brown, a worker/organizer employed by the Social Action Centre who subsequently became one of the most influential leaders of the cooperatives. He remembered some of the feelings which led him to embrace the cooperative movement:

> I used to watch the system, how people didn't have any control over their own lives. I saw how some were trying to manipulate the people, because they couldn't read and write. And I grew up hating the system.

He went on to recall a number of incidents in his own life which had impressed on him the social indifference of Jamaican society towards the sugar workers and the inequities suffered by them.

> My next move was to the staff club (at Frome) where I worked for a year. That was what you may call a very subservient position as a barman there. At the bar, you had to serve the people who were white first before a black, even if the black man came first to the bar. You would have to serve first those of higher rank, the manager before his assistant. It was a condition there at

the bar. Then you had to call each
person Mister or Miss even if the
people were of the same age. I remember there was a fellow by the name of
Caudill James. We used to be good
friends; we used to play cricket
together and track together. And he
came to the club one day-- he had just
got his job as a bookkeeper on the farm
--and I said "Caud, what happened?" And
I was reprimanded for it, for calling
him Caudill. I was supposed to say Mr.
James." Those were some of the things
that led me to revolt against the
system.

I remember playing table tennis for
WISCO. Our table at the factory club
was an old scruffy table. I used to
play doubles with a guy named Charles
Dickinson and this guy was a staff, but
we couldn't play together unless he
came to the factory workers' club. I
couldn't go to the staff club to
practice with him, and yet we were
supposed to play doubles. These were
some of the things that made me more
conscious of what the estate system
stood for. The way the people on the
estate have been treated, the barracks
they live in compared to the staff
homes, the staff who were working for
the same company. These practices made
me revolt against the system.

Matthias Brown was eventually employed in the
Tractor and Transport Department at Frome. After the
co-ops were established he was elected Vice-Chairman
of the Managing Committee of that department. He also
served on the Estate Board and the Central Board, he
was the Chairman of the Central Board's Education
Committee and worked as a Member Service Officer at
Frome. He was among those workers who rose above the
fear to become strong, never afraid to speak their
mind, fiercely defending the rights of the workers.
Another such person was Beryl Davis who was the first
woman to head an estate-level committee, the Education
Committee, at Frome. In her words:

131

A leader can't be a fearful person; a
leader has to be a genuine person and
honest. But still on the other hand
you must be furious when it comes to an
attack. I met plenty of abuses, but
that still doesn't faze me. When they
abuse me it makes me strong. I don't
fear; I don't care as long as I'm in
the right.

Above all, the estate system brought forth widespread and deep-seated anger in the sugar workers
which the organizers could draw on in their critique
of the old order and their call for a new one. But
all anger could not be easily tapped for organized
support of the cooperative system. As SAC organizer
Joe Owens put it:

When there were strikes called, it was
always the cane cutters (who responded
first), and of course they controlled
the most critical part of the industry,
the harvesting, where time is of the
essence. They were militant as hell,
even if they came down from the hills
just for a period of months. They were
always quite ready to strike. And,
they were always the ones who were
willing to take out their machetes and
go after them. But it was a sort of
wild and undisciplined type of anger.
It wasn't the kind of anger you could
build cooperatives on. The cane
cutters were the hardest to organize.

In addition to the plantation system, which no
doubt had the most profound impact on the sugar
workers' consciousness, the wider economic and political structure of Jamaican society also influenced
their thinking.

Party Politics and Religion

Jamaican society has been dominated by a two-
party system since the late 1930's with the two
parties, the Jamaica Labour Party and the People's
National Party, alternating in power (2). Everyday
life for Jamaicans is permeated with party politics,
which intensifies to a feverish pitch every four years

or so at election time when songs become political, colors become political and even the beer you drink will identify you as a supporter of one or the other party. As Stone puts it:

> The very idea of politics is for most members of the mass public synonymous with party politics. Power is seen as "party determined." Access to material benefits and opportunities by the masses (denied by the rigid and unequal social structures) are seen as opened up through party connections and party patronage (3).

Supporters of both parties suffer from a messiah complex, so to speak, which has dominated Jamaican electoral politics for a long time. There is a general acceptance of an unequal class structure which legitimizes formally educated middle-class figures like Michael Manley, Hugh Shearer or Edward Seaga as spokespersons for the masses. This is reflected in the religiously couched biblical symbolism surrounding the party leader, especially at election time. Michael Manley is "Joshua" and Edward Seaga promises "deliverance." But such a system is also highly volatile given the limited capacity or willingness of either party to truly deliver material benefits (e.g., a job or a house) to the impoverished majority of the population. According to Stone:

> Mass attitudes to party politics and politics are therefore fraught with distrust and ambivalence disguised by ritual fervor. On the one hand, party politics...is a source of hope and a means of survival for many, however inadequate the benefits received. On the other hand, the rules of the game are not fully understood. The well-off and well-to-do seem always to be prospering, and those who control power seem to grow fat on privilege. Cynicism underlies some of the surface fervor evoked by emotional political appeals ...Commitment to party politics, however emotion laden and expressive, is always partial, as party politics for the most part can only

133

supplement rather than determine the
struggle for individual survival in a
harsh environment of poverty, low and
uncertain incomes, limited opportunities and competitive interpersonal
contentions for scarce resources (4).

This distrust and ambivalence toward party
politics was also evident among the sugar workers.
Many sugar workers, especially older ones, have
remained remarkably loyal to the Jamaica Labour Party,
while others are unwilling to place themselves firmly
in one or the other camp. A minority of the Frome
workers were firmly with the PNP while the percentage
of PNP supporters undoubtedly was higher at Bernard
Lodge (5). The loyalty of so many sugar workers to
the JLP dates back to the 1938 riots and the founding
of the BITU by Sir Alexander Bustamante. The workers
remember Bustamante as the man who came to their aid
in 1938 while they claim that Norman Manley, the
founder of the NWU and the PNP, was working for
WISCO's "Big Men." They claim that Norman Manley had
referred to the sugar workers then as "cane piece
rats." This, many of them say, is the main reason why
they still vote for the JLP. The PNP's election
victory in 1972 came through the support of a broad
cross section of the population, including many sugar
workers (6).

But for other sugar workers it didn't make much
difference which party was in power, since to them it
seemed that in either case the "Big Men" would remain
on top and the "small people" would continue to
suffer. Although the PNP ideology did provide support
for the cooperatives in the statements made by Prime
Minister Michael Manley himself and by other party
leaders favoring worker participation and the idea of
cooperatives, internally the PNP struggled with widely
varied interpretations of what democratic socialism
actually meant. It was not until the annual party
conference in 1979 that a more detailed document was
adopted. This document attempted to define the PNP's
concepts of class alliance and mixed economy. The
party asserts that the interest of the working-class
must predominate and that the public sector must play
a leading role in the economy (although a vigorous
private sector was also to be supported) (7). The
PNP's initial lack of clarity was readily exploited by
the opposition which did not hesitate to frighten the

Jamaican people with the specter of communism. This served to increase ideological confusion among the co-op members.

Although the co-op organizers and leaders saw the cooperative movement among the sugar workers as a movement independent of either major political party, the sugar cooperatives very quickly came to be identified with Manley and the PNP by both supporters and opponents alike. Joe Owens recalls his early days as a SAC organizer at Monymusk:

> I appeared on the scene in April 1972. At that time, I was perceived by many as sent by the Manley government. Of course all the PNP people were very receptive to that, but even JLP people, enough of them, had some idea of what the possibilities were, so they took an interest as well. Of course, I had had no consultation with the government about doing this at all. I remember very distinctly, when Manley was elected, that the general opinion of the Jamaicans I knew was that he was no different from previous leaders at all. They thought that the difference was just a matter of style and language, but that the substance was basically the same. And Manley went on to prove us wrong.

It was quite clear, however, that where the opposition was fierce, it was coming from pro-JLP individuals and groups. Matthias Brown undertook to organize the three farms at Frome which were not prepared to go cooperative in 1976. In his analysis,

> They (the three farms) were the most difficult farms. They were so because they had more pro-JLP people on the farms there; 90-95 percent were supporters of the Jamaica Labour Party. At that time the Jamaica Labour Party did not support the cooperative movement. In fact, it was hostile to the cooperative movement, and because of that these people didn't prepare to go cooperative.

135

We had a stiff, stiff competition
between the people who wanted the co-op
and those who didn't want the co-op.
And there was a man by the name of
Labour Bull, who was a staunch Labourite. He didn't like the cooperative at
all. In fact, he didn't believe that
the workers would get the severance pay
at all. (He said) it was a lie, it was
propaganda building up for the election
in 1976. And while I was there talking
to some people in the field he came to
me and said we must leave the cane
field, because we are liars. I refused
to leave and the man was there arguing.
He tried to lead me into a political
clash. He said it was a Manley co-op
and that Manley was trying to rob the
people's money. So we got into an
argument and the man gave me one box
(punch). I never retaliated and I got
around to use that man to be one of my
staunch right hand (supporter) on the
farm until he left. Once he got his
severance he left the farm, but he did
do some organizing so as to bring the
people into the co-op.

This incident illustrates how political arguments were
used by the opposition who tried to discredit the
co-op as a "PNP or Manley thing." But as the incident
also shows, JLP supporters could be convinced of the
advantages of a cooperative. In fact, a large number
of co-op leaders belonged to the JLP camp, while
remaining ardent supporters of the cooperative. For
example, of Frome's eleven Managing Committee Chairpersons, seven supported the JLP. On the Central
Board, six of its eleven members were JLP supporters.
These individuals were critical of the PNP for several
reasons; some of them preferred housing built on
individual plots to suit individual tastes rather than
the PNP's emphasis on housing developments (although
these involved individually owned homes), and some of
them believed that the PNP was anti-religious (i.e.
they had accepted the JLP's charge that the PNP was
communist and therefore, by extension, anti-religious). They held strongly to the principle that the
cooperative was not tied to either party. Some of the
leaders also continued to support the JLP in the

belief that if the party won in the 1980 elections, government support for the cooperatives would continue.

Among the general membership, however, the majority of Labour Party sympathizers would say that the co-op didn't belong to them, whereas the PNP supporters closely identified themselves with their business. Disruption and sabotage of production and cooperative principles came from the JLP camp, and discontent concerning conditions in the co-op was often expressed in terms of criticism against Manley and the PNP. The PNP adherents supported the co-op, not simply because it was seen as sponsored by the government, but because they sincerely believed that worker ownership and control was to the benefit of the workers.

> Some people see what I (have) done was because of my political affiliation, which is not so. I always put the cooperative before everything. I have taken a lot of decisions contrary to the policies of PNP. I defend the co-op, not because I'm a PNP, but because I know that the co-op is good for the members. I supported the PNP because they have supported the co-op.
> (Matthias Brown)

Among the top executives of the Frome Monymusk Land Company and the government bureaucrats, most of whom were PNP supporters, one could find ambivalence and contradictory behavior. (This was also true of local PNP politicians.) Although they had to publically declare their support for the cooperatives, their actions frequently coincided with the interests of the estate- and farm-level staff most of whom were JLP-affiliated. Generally they were opposed to the interests of the co-op members regardless of their own political persuasion. In many instances, the class interests of both members and top level officials overrode the issue of party membership, again illustrating that neither party truly represented working class interests. Party politics was generally seen as disruptive by the co-op leaders, and some of them did their best to rise above it:

I know it is difficult. There is a
good doctor over there and you go to
the doctor. The doctor has the best
medicine in the world, he's the best
surgeon in the world, but because you
don't like him, you don't call the
medicine good. I know that you have
that difficulty in the co-op. But my
duty is to help the man. If the man is
a PNP and there is a benefit for him,
he's going to get it. And if the man
is a Labour man and he's to get a
benefit, he will get it. And if he
doesn't belong to any of the parties
and there is a benefit for him, he's
going to get it. Because I always
continue to hold to the practice that
you can be a member of a cooperative,
and no political, religious or racial
(affiliation) is supposed to change the
pattern of relations between members.
And I continue to hold that rule. I
don't go out there and discuss politics
with the members unless I'm off my job
and they want to discuss politics.
(Member Service Officer and PNP member)

In the Jamaican cultural tradition, religion
plays a central role, especially among the poorest
farm and urban workers. Much of religious thinking
reflects the same sense of powerlessness one finds in
the political arena. The respect for authority and
expertise is justified by quotations from the Bible:

The Bible says that you must show
respect towards those that are placed
over you. (Managing Committee Chairperson)

This statement was made, not to validate the Chairperson's own position of authority, but to criticize
members who had not shown proper respect toward the
farm's Project Manager. Some members would refer to
Joe Owens or Matthias Brown as "prophets of the
cooperative movement" and after the cooperatives were
destroyed they felt most keenly the loss of these
"prophets" who could no longer speak for them. For
others, however, religion gave them inspiration for
active involvement in co-op development. Managing

138

Committee meetings, for example, were always begun with a prayer. The majority of the co-op leaders and the active members were also regular church goers and would find support for cooperative principles in the Bible:

> We as workers then, whenever anything happens to anyone, we should be involved. Let's face the fact, <u>we are all our brother's keeper</u>. That's the way the cooperative works. So that is the principle I try hard to introduce at Albany (farm) and keep up with, because if we are divided, it is no good. (Beryl Davis)

Cooperative Ideology

The progressive co-op leaders and members worked to increase the power of the members in the cooperatives by forging a stronger sense of unity and commitment. They understood both the divisive and the unifying aspects of the plantation mentality and the political and religious ideologies adhered to by the members. They continually criticized the "backward" elements and built on the positive features. But their strongest ideological weapon was the ideology of the cooperative movement itself. The thinking embodied in the cooperative structure was a radical departure from the rigid authoritarian plantation mentality in which workers are considered mere instruments for producing sugar cane. The cooperatives were established to meet the needs of the members with explicit recognition of certain fundamental rights:

> Regardless of race, color or religion, cooperatives recognize the following as fundamental rights of each individual. The right to:
>
> - Life, liberty and the pursuit of personal development, well-being and happiness.
>
> - Opportunity for maximum education, limited only by ability to learn.

- Employment opportunity and security
  of livelihood sufficient for each to
  live in dignity and decency.

- Security from the economic effects of
  catastrophic illness, accident or
  economic dislocation.

- Sufficient income in retirement for
  dignity.

- Complete health services, regardless
  of age or economic status.

- Equal access to public places or
  activities.

- Be recognized and treated as more
  than an instrument for production
  (8).

Basic to the cooperative movement are also the beliefs
that:

- The most humane objectives of society
  are met when its activities are
  directed towards the common good,
  i.e., no part of society should gain
  at the expense of the others.

- Society is served best when the
  fruits of its economic, social and
  cultural accomplishments are widely
  distributed.

- The democratic system requires
  widespread participation in all of
  the important economic, political and
  cultural processes; control of these
  processes is the privilege and
  responsibility of the people as a
  whole, and not of a select part of
  the population.

- True democracy can be attained only
  if the individual is informed and
  able to give enlightened leadership
  (9).

The most radical departure from the plantation structure is the requirement that a cooperative be democratically managed:

> Their affairs should be administered by
> persons elected or appointed in a
> manner agreed by the members and
> accountable to them. Members of
> primary societies should enjoy equal
> rights of voting (one member, one vote)
> and participating in decisions affect-
> ing their societies (10).

Democracy is to be strengthened through economic
self-reliance and diversification of production,
through decreased dependence on governmental bureau-
cracies and by promoting cooperative ownership in the
sugar and other industries.

Cooperative ideology represented a major threat
to some of the most powerful economic and political
institutions in Jamaica, particularly private business
enterprise, the governmental bureaucracy and the two
major unions. Little wonder, then, that the area of
member education became a major battle ground on which
some of the fiercest battles were being fought.

Uphill Struggle

It is often said that in a revolutionary transformation of a society, the actual physical transfer
of power is the easy part. The real struggle begins
with the process of implementing the revolutionary
ideology throughout the whole system. For the cooperatives, obtaining legal ownership of the estate lands
for some 5000 sugar workers seemed relatively simple
when compared to the difficulties encountered later
when co-op leaders tried to use this legal ownership
to transform the whole plantation system. As we have
seen, the economic and political difficulties were
enormous.

For those who continued to work for the autonomy
and profitability of the co-ops, education of the
members was the principal weapon. The majority of the
members had passed one of the first requirements for
making the co-ops a reality, a test to ascertain their
understanding of cooperative principles. Now that
understanding had to be reinforced by putting the

141

ideas of worker management and workplace democracy into actual practice. Much more education was necessary. It also has to be remembered that the sugar cooperatives represented a pioneering effort to provide adult education for the sugar workers in Jamaica. Whether privately or government owned, estates were run by those who saw sugar workers merely as a means towards an end, i.e., sugar production; the workers' sole purpose was to perform the manual part of cane cultivation on orders from management. From that point of view education of the workers was obviously a waste of time and resources. Thus, as was to be expected, much of the conflict in the cooperatives was centered on who would control their educational services.

After the cooperatives were established, the government bureaucracy was forced to accept, at least in theory, that it was necessary for members to receive continued education and training. But to remain in control over cooperative affairs, the government, through its Ministry of Agriculture and the Cooperative Department, had to control the education effort. Concurrently, the Social Action Centre and its organizers were prepared to sustain their education effort launched during the initial organizing period. They maintained the viewpoint that it was essential to not only educate the leaders and members in cooperative principles and management as well as the technical operation of the farms, but also to provide them with an understanding of the need for independence from governmental or other outside direction, and an understanding of broader political issues.

> One basic message that we continually struggled to get across was the need to be independent of government, independent of that demeaning type of party subservience that has been the bane of Jamaican politics for so long. I mean the idea that there is a sacrosanct leader and that politicians, because they hold certain positions in the party, almost deserve to be worshipped. It was a constant struggle to get the workers to realize that they have as much sense as any of these party bureaucrats, though they may not have

as much power or money. It was a
constant struggle to get them to make
their first loyalty to themselves and
not to the government. There were
other things also. Before the government came out as more or less democratic socialist, we tried to get people to
think that way, and to realize that
co-ops by themselves were just islands
in an otherwise capitalist economy and
would not be able to go very far on
their own. (Joe Owens)

While there was partial agreement on the ideological level among the PNP government, the Social Action
Centre and the co-op leadership, the actions of some
party members and bureaucrats clearly indicate that
they were never willing to accept worker control, only
participation. Although the Social Action Centre
found the government's pronouncements useful as a way
to legitimize its activities and to make them respec-
table, so to speak, the government became their major
foe.

After the cooperatives had been registered, the
Social Action Centre's education effort had shifted
from leadership training in Kingston and elsewhere to
educating both leaders and members on the farms. Joe
Owens explains why:

The leadership training became much
more difficult. The leaders were more
ready to do the training when the
cooperatives were not in existence and
when their existence depended on how
much leadership training they got. The
leaders were less ready for the training after the cooperatives got started.
First of all, the people who were most
likely to receive training were people
who were largely very busy with work in
the co-op, and taking them away for 2
or 3 days as they used to was much more
difficult. But further, they just felt
that they knew enough now and what they
didn't know they could learn on the
job. And they did learn a lot. Those
that were on the Managing Committees
learned a lot very fast, because they
were dealing with problems every day in

143

a way in which they had never dealt
with them before. They had to make
decisions. So there was a lot of
on-the-job training.

The Member Service Officers, many of them former SWCC
organizers, were in charge of education and continued
to work closely with SAC. At the same time as the
need for more education shifted increasingly toward
the broad membership on the farms, the government
through a few of its officers was trying very hard to
exclude the Social Action Centre from the cane fields.
The Cooperative Department had its own officers out in
the fields, who generally limited their education
program to imparting knowledge about cooperative
principles and management. However, according to the
organizers and co-op leaders sympathetic to the Social
Action Centre the actual undermining of SAC did not
come from these field officers but from the head of
the Cooperative Department, Cedric McCulloch, and the
Minister of Agriculture, A. U. Belinfanti.

> They were trying to exclude the Social
> Action Centre from the field. There
> was a continual tug of war going on
> between SAC and the Co-op Department as
> to who was going to run the programs.
> The workers were caught in the middle,
> not knowing which side to pick or what
> to choose. Because of that tension and
> the tug of war, unfortunately not a lot
> of education was going on during that
> period. That's when I went to meeting
> after meeting and put our case forward.
> I didn't get rebuffed openly, but just
> sort of "Sorry Joe, we'll consider it."
> It was obvious that they were under
> pressure politically not to deal too
> closely with the Social Action Centre.
> (Joe Owens)

Much of the conflict was hidden to the extent that
even the Social Action Centre organizers could only
surmise what was taking place from the visible effects. Their feeling was that Cedric McCulloch
personally had gained the confidence of some key
people at Monymusk and Bernard Lodge and used them to
get some of the farms to reject SAC's education
programs. The Social Action Centre did manage to keep

the support of the majority of Central Board members.
Much of the opposition continued to come from Bernard
Lodge, where McCulloch had the most influence for some
time.

> The Bernard Lodge people were the ones
> with the most doubts (about SAC).
> That's where McCulloch did most of his
> work, because he could get to Bernard
> Lodge easier. It was just a short
> drive from Kingston. He had managed to
> raise more questions with the workers
> there at Bernard Lodge than at any
> place else. (Joe Owens)

In 1977, a Cooperative Development Centre (CDC)
was set up within the Cooperative Department. The
Minister of State for Cooperatives in the Ministry of
Agriculture, Desmond Leakey, appointed Cedric McCul-
loch to head the CDC in spite of objections from both
the Cooperative Department and the sugar cooperatives.
The cooperatives sent telegrams to Prime Minister
Michael Manley and to Minister of Agriculture A.U.
Belinfanti. The telegrams contained the following
message:

> We strongly protest Desmond Leakey's
> decision to force upon the sugar
> cooperatives Cedric McCulloch and other
> FMLCO officers to whom workers have
> already voiced strenuous objections
> because of their antisocialist and
> anti-worker mentality and practices.
> Please act to halt all appointments of
> these persons to Cooperative Department
> posts. The struggle to build socialism
> is long and hard. Let us not shrink
> from it at this crucial moment.

The telegram was signed by Stanford Phillips, Chairman
of the Central Board, and Central Board members and
Estate Chairmen Lloyd Vassell (Monymusk), Cecil
"Police" Campbell (Frome) and Sydney "Fire" Jones
(Bernard Lodge). Neither Manley nor Belinfanti acted
on the issue. Cedric McCulloch was allowed to become
the head of the CDC, and the Central Board felt
powerless to take any further action.

The Social Action Centre organizers found it more and more difficult to work directly on the farms. They continued to work with each estate's Member Service Officers by helping them to prepare educational materials, and they conducted seminars and classes for groups of cooperators. But the Member Service Officers, swamped with demands for other services, had too little time for educational work. Funds were limited and there was little or no cooperation from the other staff.

In September of 1977, the Central Board decided to appoint Joe Owens Member Services Coordinator for Education, but the advisor to the Board from the Ministry of Agriculture objected and said that the Board would first have to consult the Minister of State in the Ministry of Agriculture, Desmond Leakey before Owens could be appointed "because it may conflict with the policies of the government (11)." In December the Central Board received a letter from the Parliamentary Secretary in the Ministry Agriculture, Jim Thompson, stating that the Cooperative Development Centre was to be responsible for the education and training of the cooperators. The Board, knowing that it would have to rely on the SIA and the government for financial support especially with the impending severance deposit problem, was again unable to fight back. The government's position on the Social Action Centre's involvement in co-op education was further clarified at a high-level meeting held between top officials from the Prime Minister's Office, the Ministry of Agriculture, the Sugar Industry Authority, the BITU and the NWU, as well as the Cooperative Department. The NWU representative, C. Dunkley, made it clear that the union could not accept government endorsement of SAC:

We are not prepared to contemplate government giving passive, explicit or any other form of recognition to the Social Action Centre.

Belinfanti responded that "so far as we are concerned we do not recognize the Social Action Centre officially." But he went on to admit that the CDC was not fully staffed yet and that they were having problems getting positions filled. At the same time, he made it clear that he was going to use the financial clout of the Ministry to get rid of the Social Action Centre and Joe Owens in particular. When the NWU representative H. Thompson informed him that Joe Owens had been at an Estate Board meeting at Monymusk quite recently even after the Ministry had informed the Board that the CDC was to control co-op education, he replied:

> We will have to see into that situation. The fact of the matter is that although the cooperatives are legal entities and can operate, the fact is that we have to be subsidizing them and it has got to be a clear cut situation and we have got to use -- although this is not in the Cooperative Law -- but we have got to use our forum. We will be laying down the guidelines. I did not know that despite your letter (12) this was still happening so we will act on it (13).

In January, the Central Board officially acknowledged that Cedric McCulloch and the CDC would administer and present a cooperative education program. No comprehensive program was ever forthcoming, however. In December of 1978, almost a full year later, a Central Board member complained that the Education Committee of the Central Co-op met in Kingston every month, but that there was no education out on the farms.

The irony of the dispute between the Social Action Centre and the government and unions was that SAC de-emphasized explicitly political education in favor of business management skills. During the two years after the cooperatives were established, Joe Owens and other SAC members made a serious effort to build a strong economic education program linked to a new system of budget control developed by Michael Blakely, an accounting expert the USWCC had hired on a temporary basis. A large part of Owens' energy was spent on producing materials which would make the new system easily comprehensible to the cooperators. The rejection of Owens as education director for the Central Co-op doomed that effort, and a few years were to pass before a similar program was developed at Bernard Lodge and Monymusk.

Several SAC organizers criticized themselves in retrospect for not having put more emphasis on political ideology:

> We would have had to have made more conscious efforts to develop in the workers' leadership a level of consciousness with a stronger ideological component. We definitely steered away from it at that time. (Horace Levy)

The SAC organizers would also partially blame themselves for having lost out in the fight:

> The cooperatives had been so organized that there wasn't any room for us in them, which was a major mistake. We had organized it that way. We had insisted on worker control, and had legislated ourselves out of the thing, as though we didn't have a role alongside and for workers. Because clearly, even if one is not a worker oneself one can perform a function within a worker organization. Not only can, one ought to. I don't see one performing it anywhere but inside it. We idealistically carried this worker control thing to the point where we legislated ourselves totally out of it.
> (Horace Levy)

While the tug-of-war between the Social Action Centre and the Ministry of Agriculture and the unions was going on, another battle was raging over who was to control education for the sugar workers. This battle involved a grant from the Inter-American Foundation (IAF), a liberal development aid agency financed by the United States government. The IAF had funded early co-op organizing efforts through the Social Action Centre. Several Central Board members, including Stanford Phillips, Iseah Senior and Matthias Brown, General Secretary Winston Higgins, and SAC members approached the IAF for a grant to fund a large-scale education program on the three estates. The Cooperative Department was deliberately excluded from participating in the preparation of the grant application.

In early 1977, discussions were held between IAF representatives and the Minister of Agriculture, Belinfanti. The Ministry insisted that the funds be allocated through itself since -- as Desmond Leakey put it -- "the government wants education to be properly geared." In June, the IAF withdrew their grant offer because of its policy not to grant funds to third parties or governmental organizations. The co-op did not give up this time, however, and another grant proposal was submitted to the Inter-American Foundation in 1978. By this time, SAC's involvement in education had been reduced to a minimum, and the CDC was officially in charge of co-op education. The Ministry still insisted that education funds should be controlled by them. The Central Board continued to put pressure on the Ministry officials, visiting Belinfanti's office:

> We never gave up. We continued to have meetings with the Minister, and we continued to exert pressure. And I remember one day the Board went to see Belinfanti in his office. The members went there and literally forced the Minister. I cursed (and I) knocked my hand on the desk. And (we were) going on like we were mad. The Minister finally agreed that the co-ops would get the money from the IAF.
> (Matthias Brown)

Even after Belinfanti agreed that the cooperatives would receive the money directly from the IAF, the issue was not yet settled. In the same year, jurisdiction over the Cooperative Department was moved to the Ministry of Regional and Parliamentary Affairs. Plans for restructuring the sugar cooperatives were drawn up. One Ministry official who was also a member of the restructuring committee, L. Lindsey, made a last-ditch effort to get government control over the IAF grant. He wanted the IAF funds to be used not only for co-op education but for community organizations as well, and he managed to sway a majority of the Central Board members in favor of his plan. Two of the members from Frome, "Suk" Davis and Matthias Brown, argued against it on several grounds: it was contrary to the agreement with the IAF that the money should go straight to the grant applicant; it would limit the amount of education reaching the members of

the co-op; the money would be handled in a bureaucratic fashion. And they maintained that:

> This is not going to be good for our
> free and democratic association with
> our members. The history of the
> involvement of the government in the
> co-ops proves that it is another way of
> controlling the co-ops.

The rest of the board members were not persuaded, but
they agreed to leave the final decision to the IAF.
The foundation's representative, Steve Vetter, reaf-
firmed that the funds could not be controlled by the
third party. Thus, in the latter half of 1979, the
cooperatives could finally begin developing their own
member education program. And only by 1980 could a
comprehensive education program be launched on all
three estates, a full four years from the time the
main group of cooperatives began their operation.

Transforming the Minds of the People

Despite these ongoing conflicts, the cooperatives
had been providing the sugar workers with a number of
educational services which had been previously unavailable. Numerous seminars were held for literate
cooperators who were to then educate their co-workers
out in the field. These seminars enlightened the
workers by placing their current struggles in a
historical perspective, and it informed them about the
history of the Sugar Workers' Cooperative Council.
There were accounting, budgeting and co-op management
seminars; payroll classes and budget control classes
were held on some ten farms. Various seminars sponsored by foreign foundations and governments together
with the Cooperative Department and the USWCC were
attended by co-op members from all three estates.
Furthermore, cooperators visited Cuba and Panama (14)
as official representatives of the sugar cooperatives
and invited guests of the two governments. Matthias
Brown was sent to Israel on a six-month course in
cooperative development, and later several other
cooperators and a few staff went to Canada, Hungary
and Lesotho for training in cooperative management.
For many, traveling to seminars and courses within
Jamaica and abroad was the most memorable and valuable
experience that the co-op had offered them, allowing

them to see new places and to meet people from different walks of life.

Beginning in 1976, a newspaper for sugar workers, Workers' Time, was published on a fairly regular basis by a group of co-op and SAC members. The paper was aimed at informing and educating the sugar workers about developments in the cooperatives, the sugar industry and Jamaica, as well as international news of special concern to sugar workers. The paper was also designed to counter what was generally biased and unfavorable information about the cooperatives in the two major daily newspapers, The Gleaner in particular. Workers' Time provided a forum for co-op members to express their views; it reported production and other economic data for individual farms and the three estates; it praised significant accomplishments, such as diversification efforts of various farms; it exposed corruption among members and staff; and it informed members of the actions taken by the Central Board and the action or inaction of government ministries and the SIA. Every issue also contained an educational spread, illuminating special problems confronting the co-ops in cartoon form, easily understood by those unable to read. But courses, seminars and Workers' Time only reached a minority of the five thousand co-op members; illiteracy and ignorance about cooperative management and large-scale business affairs remained high. This ignorance continued to act as a major cause of disunity on the farms. Most information was still communicated through word of mouth, and rumors could be easily spread.

The education program, funded by the IAF for a three-year period and launched in early 1980, was clearly a step forward for the co-ops in the sense that the USWCC's own Education Department was in control of the program. The department now could -- and did -- decide to ask both the Social Action Centre and the CDC for assistance.

The main aims of the program were:

> (a) Improving Cooperative Management: This will involve getting rid of the relics of the old estate system, some dating back to slavery times, and implementing proper cooperative management

151

especially in the area of work
distribution and farm organization.

(b) Developing Full Human Potential:
The idea here is education geared
towards self-improvement. Many
cooperators for example lack basic
reading and writing skills. This
must be reversed...

(c) Viability:
Concepts such as productivity and
cost controls must be given to
workers so that they can be
translated into greater efficiency
in production and finance.

(d) Greater Understanding of Business:
Internal business operation,
sources of finance, the national
economy and the importance of the
industry will be dealt with here.
The international sugar situation
will also be discussed.

(e) Increased Understanding of Wider
Social and Political Positions:
This involves education about the
wider society so that cooperators
can assess their position in it
and the contributions they can
make (15).

The planning document went on to say that "the use of
the principle of the <u>worker being used to teach his</u>
<u>fellow worker may be the best guarantee for success</u>
<u>of the</u> program."

The Director of the education program, Lennie
Ruddock, hired on the recommendations made by some of
the Central Board advisors, was a former civil servant
who had held a position in the Ministry of Education.
He was to administer a staff of 15 people and to
prepare educational materials for them. On each of
the three estate co-ops, a Senior Training Officer
chosen by the Director supervised four field staff who
were to conduct literacy and business management
classes on the farms. At the insistence of the

152

Chairman of the Central Board's Education Committee, Matthias Brown, the field instructors were hired from among the educated members of sugar workers' families. The education field staff were also to help train peer leaders from among the membership, who would then teach their fellow cooperators business management, finance and production. The idea of peer-leadership training was an effort to break away from the traditional colonial system of authoritarian, or at best paternalistic, teachers spoon-feeding students with knowledge deemed important by school administrators and teachers. The education program was an ambitious effort aimed at educating a maximum number of cooperators with the ultimate goal of making much of the technical and managerial staff unnecessary.

In spite of the numerous positive features built into the program, educating the sugar workers turned out to be no easy task for those directly involved in it. When actually implemented, the program was heavily focused on literacy training, while production and management training remained quite limited and sporadic; political education was completely neglected. The peer-leadership system was never fully implemented, mainly because the Director of Education insisted that peer leaders work as teachers without any additional pay, even though money for peer leaders was originally included in the budget. The peer leaders complained that the education staff was well paid for _their_ work and demanded some form of compensation.

The two main problems confronting the teaching staff were the often fierce opposition to the education program from the farm- and estate-level production staff (16) and the severe financial difficulties confronting the co-ops in their latter years of operation. Many of the employed staff, and particularly the Project Managers on the farms, continued to openly voice their opposition to membership education as they had earlier when the cooperatives were being organized. They were obviously afraid that educated co-op members would eventually be in a position to put them out of their jobs. They told the members that education was a waste of time. On many farms at Frome, the Project Manager would continue to deliberately shift members from day labor to task work so as to prevent them from attending class. Since classes were held on work time and since the day laborers would continue to collect a full day's pay even when spending some of the day in class, the only workers who would lose some of their pay if they attended class were the task workers. As a result of such manipulation the majority of the members attending classes were day laborers and therefore mostly women cultivators. One of the literacy teachers described the conflict with the staff like this:

> Now that they (the staff) saw the people getting educated, we had a fight: the education staff versus the cultivation staff. We had a problem with them; they didn't want us to educate the people. People were getting wise, and were seeing that they (the staff) weren't doing their jobs, and started to criticize them. People were now able to manage. They learned how to make their own payroll, etc. The staff didn't like that, so they started to set people against us (saying) that we were their enemies and they were their friends. In the long run, they are finding out now who are their enemies and who are their friends. So that was one thing that hampered education. (Sandra Bingham)

Many members were listening to the Project Manager and regarded the education program as foolishness. Many also felt that they were too old to learn and that they didn't need education since they had managed without it and survived. On the average about ten percent of the total co-op membership attended classes; Frome led with 16 percent participation.

The education effort was seriously restrained by the economic problems plaguing the co-ops; by 1980, the cooperatives' financial difficulties had taken on crisis proportions. Retroactive pay increases, after-crop bonus payments, interest, vacation and sick leave payments were delayed for weeks. The uncertainty about when the payments would be made and the constant, nagging shortage of cash led to turmoil and dissatisfaction among the membership; for weeks at a time, it was impossible to hold classes. The majority of the members refused to involve themselves in any activity on the farm until their payments had been received. At the same time many JLP supporters and the staff were actively undermining the members' faith in the cooperatives and the PNP.

Another factor which slowed down the work of the education staff was that the structure of the co-ops was not sufficiently different from the old plantation system. Many members were confused by the fact that the reality of how the cooperatives were run did not fit with the theory of how they were supposed to be run. The education staff and Education Committee members would try to convince the members that the cooperatives were theirs and that members should insist on their right to full participation in decision-making even in the face of opposition from staff. But the experience of the members was that real control was out of their hands; as always, the "Big Man" was in charge. The education staff urged the members to work hard and to cut costs so that they would gain in the long run from a more viable enterprise. They told the members that strikes were strikes against themselves. This was of course true, but the members saw no profits forthcoming even after they had adopted some cost-cutting measures. Strike action was reinforced by the government: often money for bonus and other payments was found only after the members refused to work or demonstrated. The members were told that they should educate themselves so that they could run the co-ops without the staff and the "Big Men", but many felt that it wasn't worth the trouble since they doubted they could ever become true owners. Because a disproportionate amount of control remained in the hands of managerial staff and government bureaucrats, the members were not inclined to drastically alter their perceptions of themselves in relationship to their former bosses. They continued to see themselves as workers rather than worker/owners.

The education program itself was suffering from some serious shortcomings. Education Director Ruddock ran the program as a top-down enterprise with decision-making centralized in the Kingston office. Education Committees were set up by the farms and estates to oversee the program, but because all the resources were in the hands of the staff, including cars or motorcycles, access to telephones, etc., the farm level committees' functions were reduced to the recruitment of students for the classes. The Director was responsible for the production of the educational materials, but it took the central office in Kingston over one yar to produce a few pamphlets on budgeting and finance to be used for peer group education in the fields. In the meantime the education staff on the estates were limited to teaching literacy classes with materials provided by the Jamaica Movement for the Advancement of Literacy (JAMAL) using traditional teaching techniques. What was worse, many teachers did little while waiting for the central office to provide them with educational material, even though they were capable of producing it themselves. Although the Director of Education no doubt had good intentions, many of the problems afflicting the program in its first year were clearly a result of his inability to overcome his own limitations, originating from his previous bureaucratic experience. Some of the education staff, farm Education Committee members and especially the Chairman of the Central Education Committee, Matthias Brown, struggled with these problems and were not afraid to criticize and offer constructive suggestions to the Director. They believed that had the cooperatives been allowed to continue to exist, they could have made the program work. In the words of Sandra Bingham, one of the Frome education staff:

> If we had had another three years, we
> would have reached very far.

While the IAF-funded program was being implemented on the farms, with much staff opposition to any SAC involvement, another educational program was conducted at Bernard Lodge and Monymusk. The Social Action Centre had been invited back by the Bernard Lodge Estate Board and an organization development program was initiated with the help of SAC and Dietrich Champaignie, a lecturer at the University of the West Indies. The program was aimed primarily at identifying the main sources of financial loss and management problems so as to improve the economic viability of the estate.

The members, staff and co-op leadership were involved directly in the identification of problems and their analysis, as well as in formulating solutions. Much of the work was done through mass meetings involving all parties concerned. Thus the members were in a position to learn about the manage-

ment process, budgeting and cost accounting while
working on concrete solutions to problems affecting
all of them. They could readily see the advantage in
increasing their knowledge of the business. The
difference in style between the hierarchical organization, favored by the co-op's Education Director, and
the SAC-sponsored organization development program
again reflects the different ideological assumptions
of government bureaucrats and SAC respectively. While
progressive looking on paper, the centrally implemented co-op education program allowed for token worker/
member participation only; the organization development program was based on the assumption of equality
for all groups involved and the right of the members
to have full participation in the decision-making
process.

Throughout the struggle to bring education to the
members of the cooperatives, there were many high
points amidst the frustration and disappointment. The
celebrations of Labour Week and Heroes' Day at Frome
in 1980 were such high points. The members participated in large numbers depicting in songs and pageants
the struggles of Jamaican workers in the past and
their own struggles of the present. One of the
teachers summed up her feelings about what she thought
she had accomplished in the first year of the program:

> The greatest success is for people to
> know what their rights are and to use
> them so that they are not being taken
> advantage of. I think that was one
> achievement when you could get some
> people to know what their rights were.

> They (the members) were once afraid.
> Some of them who didn't know their
> rights, now that they know their rights
> they will stand up and argue. You know
> once they were afraid of busha. But
> now we tell them that if they say this
> they can not be fired and so people
> stand up and speak for their rights.

Throughout 1980, until the November election, the
education staff and Education Committee members were
filled with enthusiasm and optimism for the future.
There was a definite feeling that the shortcomings of
the program could be corrected, and they were looking

forward to new diversification projects, to more members receiving training both in Jamaica and overseas, to more members assuming the responsibilities of the cultivation staff, and to more cultural events designed to forge unity among the members and to foster pride in themselves and the cooperatives.

After the elections the enthusiasm slowly turned into uncertainty and eventually into hopelessness. It quickly became clear to some of the members and staff involved in the education program that the new JLP-controlled government was in fact out to destroy the cooperatives.

1. Carl Stone, <u>Democracy and Clientelism in Jamaica</u>. (Transaction Books, 1980), p. 43.

2. A small third party, the Marxist-Leninist Workers' Party of Jamaica (WPJ), is an outgrowth of the Workers' Liberation League established in late 1974. WPJ had a small number of adherents among the co-op members, while the leading person in the sugar factory cooperative movement at Frome was a WPJ member.

3. Stone, <u>op.cit</u>, p. 81.

4. <u>Ibid</u>.

5. Bernard Lodge and Monymusk are located closer to the Kingston metropolitan area and the PNP appeal to the urban poor seems to have had an impact on the workers, especially at Bernard Lodge.

6. It is difficult to estimate the number of co-op members who voted in favor in the PNP in 1972 and 1976. By the time our study was made, criticism of the PNP had become widespread.

7. Michael Manley, <u>Jamaica: Struggle in the Periphery</u>. (Third World Media Ltd., 1982), pp. 127-8.

8. USWCC "Guidelines for Committee Members of Sugar Worker Cooperatives," p. 3.

9. <u>Ibid</u>.

10. <u>Ibid</u>., p. 4.

11. Minutes of USWCC Central Board meeting, October 4, 1977.

12. Reference to the letter sent by Jim Thompson to the Central Board in December informing the Central Board that the CDC was to be in charge of co-op education.

13. Minutes of meeting held at the Ministry of Agriculture, January 19, 1978.

14. The late General Omar Torrijos visited Jamaica in 1976 and invited a delegation of USWCC members to visit Panama.

15. USWCC Education Department, "The Sugar Cooperatives: A New Education Thrust." September 17,
1979.

16. Although the co-op education program deliberately
included an agreement that both SAC and the CDC
would make contributions in kind to match the IAF
funds, there continued to be strong opposition
among the staff (farm and estate managers)
against any direct SAC presence on the farms,
especially at Frome.

CHAPTER VI

A DEVELOPMENT STRATEGY THAT FAILED

> For almost a decade Michael Manley's socialist government was mocked by the structural dependencies of Jamaica's cash crop and raw materials export-based economy, hooked in typical neo-colonial patterns to the world trade roller-coaster. These vulnerabilities of excessive inter-linkage to a global system well beyond Manley's control reflect the pathologies of small, weak countries still addicted to such trade patterns requiring continual "fixes" of external capital infusions and causing increasing indebtedness, whether to the International Monetary Fund (IMF) or other Northern Hemisphere controlled financial institutions (1).
> (Hazel Henderson)

There are several models of economic development for Third World countries. One is the "bootstrap" industrialization by invitation pioneered by Puerto Rico, based upon tax concessions and low wages to lure foreign investment. Jamaica tried this model during the 1950's and 1960's, and again during the 1980's under the Seaga government. A second is the centrally planned socialist economy as in Cuba, where the state plays a leading role in economic planning, and all major industries and agricultural estates are government owned. A third is the reform path undertaken by the People's National Party in Jamaica between 1974 and 1980 under the banner of democratic socialism. The sugar workers cooperatives were an integral part of this program and were mentioned more than once by Prime Minister Manley as epitomizing the kind of reforms the party was committed to. In this chapter, we discuss those reforms and their outcome and contrast this reformist path with a fourth alternative of self-reliant development based upon local production for local consumption, economic decentralization and workers' control, which was missed by the PNP.

In 1972, after 20 years of foreign investment and economic growth, Jamaica was still heavily dependent on imported machinery, parts, oil and food. Profits continued to be repatriated abroad. Within the country, wealth and income were highly skewed; an upper and upper-middle class of very small proportion occupied the top, and a very large class of impoverished workers and the unemployed was found at the bottom. The JLP's program of industrialization by invitation was obviously not working. Yet, despite a vocal left wing within its own party, the newly elected PNP government was by no means ready to abandon private enterprise and move toward either the Cuban model of a state-controlled planned economy, nor the model of self-reliance, which had been adopted by the Chinese after the success of the Communist revolution in 1949.

Under the leadership of Prime Minister Michael Manley, Jamaica began to move along the reformist path (2). The PNP programs differed from those of the JLP in that they enlarged the role of the state in the economy and included land reform as well as expanded government welfare services. Moving cautiously toward the left, Manley announced in 1974 that the PNP was committed to democratic socialism based on a mixed economy of private and public enterprise. One of the government's first acts was to vastly enlarge its share of revenues from bauxite, its most profitable natural resource. It nationalized one bank and about half the major hotels, and extended government ownership of transportation and utilities. At the same time, it approved the transformation of the Frome, Monymusk and Bernard Lodge estates into workers' cooperatives. Soon thereafter, the government also purchased the major sugar factories on those estates, placing them under the administration of the National Sugar Company. In order to understand the failure of Manley's reforms, we need to describe the economic context in which they were undertaken.

Sugar Production and Foreign Exchange

As we have seen in the preceding chapters, the sugar workers' cooperatives were beset by many problems, including excess manpower, old machinery, inadequate capital and credit, illiteracy, droughts and floods, and the vulnerability of monocrop agriculture to the spread of disease. (The estates, acting on the advice of the Sugar Industry Research Institute, had planted large quantities of one high-yield variety of cane that turned out to be very susceptible to the rust and smut diseases that hit the farms in the 1970's.) The biggest problem for the co-ops, however, and indeed for the entire industry, was the unfair terms of trade involved in sugar export.

Given the nature of the contemporary world trade system, the production of sugar and other agricultural commodities is generally disadvantageous for third world countries. The prices for imports such as machinery, fertilizer and herbicides as well as those of sugar exports are set in London, New York, or other Western metropolitan centers. Under the terms of the International Sugar Agreement subscribed to by the European Economic Community (EEC), the third world sugar-producing countries were given quotas, which in the case of Jamaica provided a guaranteed export market for some 120,000 tons of sugar per year at preferential rates. In 1978, for example, sugar exported to the EEC brought a price of about U.S.$330 per ton, double the world market price of U.S.$160 per ton. The very existence of subsidy prices and quotas helps underscore the dependency of the producers; the possibility of reduced subsidies or export quotas is an ever present threat. Jamaica's inability to meet all of its export quota in 1978 under the International Sugar Agreement resulted in a cut in its quota for future years.

The terms of trade have become increasingly unfavorable to producers of commodities such as sugar. For example, it takes more tons of sugar each succeeding year to purchase one tractor. Further, competition from beet sugar and high fructose corn syrup produced in Europe and America has been exerting a downward influence on cane sugar prices. The production of cane sugar for export under these conditions forces the increased use of mechanization resulting in "efficient" farms operated by a much reduced workforce. "Viability" of the cane sugar industry thus means fewer jobs and an ever increasing dependence on expensive imports. There is no escape from this trade trap for commodity exporting nations unless they form producers' associations capable of controlling supplies, as did OPEC with oil, or join together to force more favorable trade conditions through moral and political pressure.

The strategy of earning foreign exchange through sugar production was a poor strategy indeed for Jamaica. World market prices for sugar fluctuated considerably during the 1960's and 1970's with short periods of high prices followed by several years of decline (see Figure 6.1). Except for occasional years of high world market prices for sugar, as in 1974, the country was producing sugar at a loss. The government paid a premium in Jamaican dollars to grow and manufacture raw sugar that would bring in precious British pounds or American dollars. In 1976, for example, the SIA lost J$26 million and in 1977, an estimated J$9 million (3).

The World Bank provided a loan of about U.S.$23 million in 1978 to rehabilitate the sugar factories at Frome, Monymusk and Bernard Lodge. According to the terms of the loan, two-thirds of this money had to be spent abroad for machinery, equipment, and consultants. Foreign exchange income from sugar exports in 1978 was U.S.$57 million. In addition to the money spent abroad for the renovation of the three factories, an estimated 40 percent of these sugar revenues left the country to pay for imports needed by the sugar industry. This includes repayment of principal and interest on the World Bank's loan to the government for the factories, money for imported fuel, fertilizer, herbicides, replacement parts, and shipping and insurance costs. The rest of the foreign exchange generated by the sugar industry was used by the government to help repay previous foreign loans and to finance the tremendous volume of imports used by the country.

The working class majority consumed some of the imports, especially food staples such as rice, but a large proportion consisted of televisions, cars, and other luxury items used primarily by the upper and upper-middle classes. The PNP government imposed import controls and tried to prevent profiteering by channeling imports of food and other staples through the State Trading Corporation. Despite these efforts, Jamaica simply did not have enough foreign exchange to pay for all of its imports. It was forced to borrow more from abroad, increasing its debt and insuring that an even greater proportion of foreign exchange would be used in future years just to pay interest on its loans (4).

164

FIGURE 6.1   WORLD SUGAR PRICES, 1960-1980

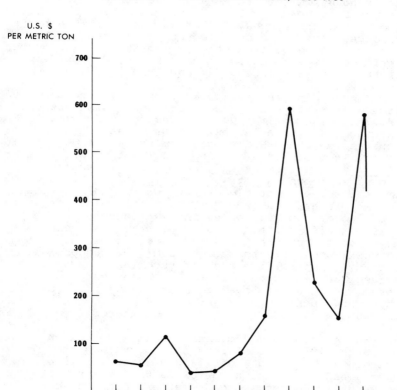

U.S. $
PER METRIC TON

SOURCES: 1980, **Sugar World**, Vol. 3, #3, 5; Idris Hamid (ed) **The World of Sugar Workers** (Trinidad: Caribbean Ecumenical Programme, 1978)

The difficulties faced by the cooperatives must be put into the context of a general decline in Jamaican sugar production during the two decades after 1965. The island's production fell from 383,000 tons in 1974 to only 204,000 tons by 1981. (See Table 6.1). The PNP government tried to stem this decline through such production incentives as replanting grants, support for the Sugar Industry Research Institute, and the renovation of the sugar factories at Frome, Monymusk and Bernard Lodge. Despite the rehabilitation of the three sugar factories made possible by the World Bank loan, and despite the government's attempts to stimulate cane production, Jamaican sugar output continued to drop during the 1970's, except for a slight increase between 1977 and 1978.

The decline in cane production on the cooperative farms was part and parcel of what was happening throughout the entire sugar industry in Jamaica. In allowing the three largest sugar estates to become cooperatives, the Manley government was engaging in "lemon socialism," turning over to the workers that part of the business abandoned by the transnational corporations because it was unprofitable. At the same time the government divided up what had previously been an integrated industry by maintaining separate control over the factories that processed the cane, resisting efforts to extend cooperative management to the processing plants. Had the farms at Frome, Monymusk and Bernard Lodge remained under direct government control instead of becoming cooperatives, the decline in production on these estates would probably have been even greater, judging from the continuing losses of the National Sugar Company which managed the factories on the three estates.

While overall Jamaican sugar production fell during the 1970's, the drop in exports was even more marked. From a high of 278,000 tons in 1974, net exports had fallen to a low of 95,000 tons by 1981; in the meantime, domestic consumption remained constant at about 100,000 tons per year (see Table 6.1). Because of the preferential price structure embodied in the International Sugar Agreement, most of the Jamaican sugar exports were sold to the EEC countries during this time period. The other major recipients were the United States and Canada (see Table 6.2).

TABLE 6.1: JAMAICAN SUGAR PRODUCTION, DOMESTIC CONSUMPTION, IMPORTS AND EXPORTS 1974–1981
(in thousands of tons)

YEAR	PRODUCTION	DOMESTIC CONSUMPTION	IMPORTS	EXPORTS	NET EXPORTS
1974	383	102	0	278	278
1975	366	105	4	265	261
1976	365	105	6	242	237
1977	296	113	16	222	206
1978	306	115	22	203	181
1979	291	101	0	194	194
1980	236	117	5	135	130
1981	204	100	29	125	95

NOTE: Detail does not always add to total because of rounding.

SOURCE: Sugar World Dec. 1982, based on International Sugar Organization Yearbook, 1981.

167

TABLE 6.2: JAMAICAN SUGAR EXPORTS, BY COUNTRY OF DESTINATION, 1975–1981
(in thousands of tons)

YEAR	EEC	U.S.	CANADA	OTHER	TOTAL
1975	132	75	0	58	265
1976	158	57	25	2	242
1977	136	57	25	2	242
1978	151	41	11	0	203
1979	87	60	32	15	194
1980	91	43	0	0	135
1981	125	0	0	0	125

NOTE: Detail does not always add to total because of rounding.

SOURCE: Sugar World Dec. 1982, based on International Sugar Organization Yearbook, 1981.

168

The current JLP government has been unable to reverse this trend. Total island sugar output in 1982 and 1983 dropped to slightly under 200,000 tons (see Figure 6.2). In consequence, Jamaica must either reduce its sugar exports or find itself in the absurd position of having to import sugar to help meet its own domestic needs.

The Limits of the PNP Reform

The PNP's domestic reforms were not very successful in furthering Jamaica's economic development. In part, this was because there was not enough structural economic change; Prime Minister Manley favored a mixed economy which meant continued encouragement of foreign investment through tax concessions and similar means. Foreign investors and local capitalists were wary of democratic socialism, however. They feared the possibility of expropriation and nationalization. There was little private investment during the PNP era; in fact there was a net disinvestment. The opposition of the local business class to the PNP reforms kept the economy at a standstill. Many enterprises, including the key bauxite industry, cut back production, and some even shut down altogether.

Further, there was no real movement away from the commitment to export commodity production. In 1978, three-fourths of the country's foreign exchange was still derived from commodity exports including bauxite, sugar and bananas (see Table 6.3). In spite of Jamaica's expanded trade with Cuba and with the CARICOM countries (Guyana, Trinidad & Tobago, and Barbados), its major trading partners were still the United States, Canada and Britain. The continuation of export commodity production, with its built-in dependency on imports, precluded balanced social and economic development. The increasing cost of imports relative to the prices of Jamaica's exports led to a widening trade gap, forcing the country to borrow ever more funds from abroad. The ongoing money shortage left the government unable to provide adequate funding for many of its social programs, and affected the cooperatives as well. The government limited its financial support of the cooperatives in part because there was simply not enough money available.

FIGURE 6.2   JAMAICAN SUGAR PRODUCTION, 1965-1983

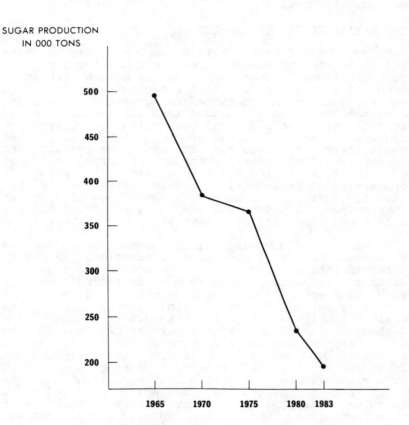

SUGAR PRODUCTION
IN 000 TONS

SOURCES: 1965-1973, **World Bank** Report; 1974-1981,
Sugar World, Dec. 1982; 1982-83, **Workers
Time**, Vol. 9, #7-8, Aug.-Sept. 1983

TABLE 6.3: INCOME FROM JAMAICAN EXPORTS, 1978

PRODUCT	INCOME U.S.$ MILLION	PERCENT
Bauxite and alumina	$575	65%
Sugar	58	7
Bananas	17	2
Tourism	87	10
Other	148	16
TOTAL	$885	100%

Also, factions within the party kept it from fully implementing more radical policies. The PNP was a coalition of center and left factions, with Prime Minister Manley serving as arbiter. The strength of the left-wing was its appeal to the masses, which garnered the votes of the working class and small farmers. Most of the party's top leadership comprised the core of the center faction which maintained ties to the upper-middle class and to some of the local capitalists, both rewarding sources of campaign funds. Thus the upper strata were most influential within the party.

Moreover, the PNP political directorate chose to rely on an essentially conservative and unimaginative bureaucracy of career civil servants. Often trained overseas, they reflected neo-colonial values and ways of thinking. Civil service officials discouraged the cooperatives from attaining economic viability through crop diversification and hindered them from developing into truly autonomous worker-controlled organizations. The influence of the government technocrats insured a watering down of any reform programs adopted by the party leadership.

A more thorough reform of the estates than that which was achieved would have entailed mobilization similar to the massive efforts that took place during the early organizing years of the SWCC. Such reforms would have necessitated general austerity and diminution of privileges for the upper strata. The dominant faction within the PNP was also unwilling to allow such mobilization for fear that it could lead to a new power base outside of the established party framework.

In trying to implement its reforms, the Manley government encountered external political opposition as well. Manley's reforms led to strong counter moves by the American-based transnational corporations, local elites, the opposition JLP, and the United States government. Local businesses shut down and laid off workers; wholesalers hoarded basic staples, which resulted in shortages; and the rich sent a steady stream of money abroad. The aluminum companies cut back their Jamaican production in response to the increased bauxite taxes and began to expand their imports from Africa. Regarding Manley's foreign policy as a threat to its hegemony in the Caribbean, the United States orchestrated a calculated economic and political destabilization campaign. Beginning in 1976, American banks were suddenly unwilling to extend credit to Jamaica; loans were cut off altogether. American government aid was cut down to a trickle.

The United States Secretary of State, Henry Kissinger, visited Jamaica during Christmas 1975, and asked Prime Minister Manley not to publicly support the presence of Cuban troops in Angola (5). When Manley refused, the United States responded with increased pressure. Manley's request for trade credits worth U.S.$100 million never materialized. A destabilization campaign was waged by the CIA apparently in collaboration with some of the JLP leaders (6). Hired gunmen set fires and then shot the people trying to escape from the burning buildings; the publicity given these and other acts of violence helped frighten away many tourists (7). The violence escalated to such an extent that Manley had to declare a state of emergency. The Prime Minister was acutely aware of the possibility of American military intervention; this may have limited his actions and kept him from pushing reforms "too far" (8).

Finally, Jamaica's desperate need for foreign exchange forced the government to borrow from the International Monetary Fund (IMF) in 1977 and 1978. The soaring cost of living which resulted from the government's compliance with IMF loan conditions contributed heavily to popular discontent which led a majority to vote the PNP out of office in 1980. The IMF demanded a devaluation of the currency and less government spending on social programs. As a result of the IMF agreement, the cost of food items, gasoline and other staples rose sharply. Increasing prices for food and transportation impacted on the poor the hardest. In 1979, the PNP tried to cut Jamaica's ties with the IMF, but by then it was too late to undo the negative effects of the agreement. It was soon voted out of office. The democratic election system often leads to a very short term in office for reformers, which means there is little time to carry development programs through to their conclusion.

Self-Reliance: The Missed Alternative

Given the dependent role into which Jamaica was forced by the nature of the world trade system, the development path of self-reliance would have been a better alternative to the limited reforms undertaken by the Manley government. Such a program would have had to be based on a commitment to greater self-sufficiency in growing food for the island's needs and an attempt to produce locally most of the inputs needed by the major industries.

It is only too easy to be critical of the Jamaican reform efforts with hindsight. Nevertheless, because we believe that cutting excessive dependence on commodity exports is essential for economic viability and social progress of third world countries, we will sketch out the broad outlines of the self-reliant alternative that the PNP might have pursued had the progressive forces within it prevailed over its center/right-wing and had the government been able to fully implement democratic socialist policies. Such a move toward self-reliance would have been possible given the necessary political leadership and a high level of popular mobilization. Moving out of the dependency trap would not have been easy for Jamaica. As Henderson says:

> Breaking such cycles of dependency would mean many years of painful withdrawal and an economic reorientation toward domestic agricultural self-reliance, local manufacturing to

173

add value to raw materials, revival of indigenous crafts and culture, and retraining of workers -- while simultaneously restructuring and forging links based on regional trade, bartering and monetary agreements. Reintegrating such economies into more localized patterns better fitted to local cultures and eco-systems could gradually replace the vagaries of the world trade system (9).

Self-reliance is a philosophy of using local initiative and resources to produce for local needs on the basis of land reform, decentralization, communal effort, and workers' control. Self-reliance is based on production for local use instead of solely for profit. Decisions are based not only on economic but also on community, social, and ecological criteria. As a strategy of development, self-reliance involves the balanced growth of agriculture and industry into a mutually interdependent network where needed inputs are purchased locally to build up the indigenous economy and to keep money from flowing out of the community and the country. Although it is not always possible to avoid the use of external capital, self-reliance is based on maximum use of "sweat equity" and internally generated capital in place of dependence on outside loans (10).

Self-reliance is one way for third world nations to counter the domination of the wealthy capitalist countries. Such dependency is inevitably exploitive, and at best aids only the small upper-middle and upper-class fraction of the population. Self-reliance implies a shift to a more egalitarian social structure. It is antithetical to hierarchies and to the exploitation of the poor masses by the rich few. It involves collective mobilization and communal effort in place of individualism, and is only possible on the basis of democratic self-management exemplified by the Jamaican sugar workers' attempts to run their own cooperatives. It is consistent with national planning, but involves decentralization and local decision-making in place of top-down commands from government centers (11). Such a program was in fact proposed for Jamaica by a group of left-wing intellectuals but never was implemented on any broad scale. A major element of that program was the establishment of

Community Enterprise Organizations, which were community-owned, cooperatively run organizations whose focus was production for local use on the basis of locally available inputs (12).

The most essential element of self-reliance is domestic production of food, so that in a crisis, food shortages cannot be used as a weapon by foreign powers. Food production should utilize an intermediate technology that does not lead to undue dependence on imported hybrid seeds, fertilizer and highly specialized machinery. Self-reliance does not necessarily imply abandoning commodity exports, but it does mean that production of food crops to meet community and national needs be given first priority in the use of prime agricultural land. This is the first step toward reversing the pattern of domination generated by colonialism, which transformed previously self-sufficient subsistence farmers into dependent low-wage producers of commodities such as coffee, cocoa, bananas or sugar, and consumers of imported food and other goods.

The Manley government did begin to stimulate food production through such programs as Project Land Lease, which enabled small farmers to grow food for domestic use on formerly idle land. It would have been relatively easy to extend this emphasis to the sugar workers' cooperatives had the government not been preoccupied with maximizing cane production for the benefit of its factories. A portion of the acreage of the three sugar estates could have been planted in food crops to augment the supply grown by private farmers.

We are not suggesting that the cooperatives should suddenly have stopped growing cane. They could, however, have taken the least productive land out of cane and put it to alternative uses. Simultaneously, they could have made a strong effort to raise the yield of the remaining acreage, so that they would have been able to produce as much cane on three-fourths of the land as they had previously on all of it. They could have begun a systematic diversification program to utilize all of their previously uncultivated land. In this way, the cooperatives might have produced both cane and food.

This approach is illustrated by the experience of Nicaragua after 1979. Post-revolutionary Nicaragua was able to grow more food staples while it also increased production of certain export commodities. By 1982, the Sandinista government had succeeded in stimulating the production of rice, corn and beans to return to the same levels they had been during 1970. Production of some export commodities actually increased after the Sandinista victory.

> Nicaraguan policy makers began to realize that "food versus export crops" was partly a false dilemma. Nicaragua could <u>both</u> produce more food for local consumption and more for export. It could increase its exports of coffee, sugar, beef and cotton primarily by using the lands already devoted to their production more efficiently and fully. In addition, Nicaragua could increase food production by providing more support and better prices for peasant producers as well as by allowing peasants and seasonal laborers to plant on idle lands (as provided under the new agrarian reform law) (13).

The Nicaraguans, however, have been severely hampered by American-sponsored military intervention, which has partially disrupted agricultural production.

The Jamaican cooperatives did begin a program of crop diversification, albeit on a very modest scale. The workers' experience with the production of rice, fish, beans, root crops and various vegetables showed that these could readily be grown using land, skills, technology and machinery already at hand. Although cane production uses much labor, especially for harvesting, most of the work is done only during the six-month-long crop season. Food farming can be several times as labor intensive. It could have provided year-round employment, added to the country's food supply (decreasing the need for food imports) and helped to guarantee the co-ops' economic viability.

A small portion of each of the 23 cooperative cane farms could have been used for integrated production of a diversity of food crops side by side and in rotation the whole year round (14). Such farms would be based on the principles of synergy, growing mutually interdependent crops, and on the conservation of natural resources. By rotating legumes with other crops, soil fertility could be maintained at a high level, with less need to add fertilizers than with cane production. Cane tops, usually destroyed by burning at harvest, could have been used to feed cows. This in turn could have formed the basis for small dairies, helping to relieve the scarcity of milk, while manure from the animals could have replaced some of the imported fertilizer used by the farms.

The addition of various agricultural processing industries could have generated additional employment and income for the cooperatives. In keeping with the philosophy of self-reliance, the emphasis in choice of process should be on a combination of intermediate technology, production for local consumption, and minimization of capital outlay. Simple processing industries would include the manufacture of peanut butter, soy flour, bean curd, cheese, corn meal, soy and sunflower oil, and sun-dried fruits.

A major key to the success of increased food production would have been the use of the sugar cooperatives themselves as the basis for a distribution mechanism. Fresh food crops and processed products could have been marketed through a system of consumer cooperatives organized by sugar co-op members, with a retail market on each farm and additional outlets in nearby villages, towns and cities. Each consumer cooperative would have provided several additional jobs. The expansion of the sugar workers cooperatives into the area of retail food distribution would have met a pressing community need, and might have helped local small farmers to overcome their marketing problems. Finally, an integrated plan of economic development could also have utilized various cane-based agro-industrial manufacturing processes to produce building board, plastics, paper, fuel alcohol, industrial chemicals, and other products (15). The main emphasis would be on medium size installations which could be constructed by the cooperatives' own members without tying them into dependence on imported components or foreign experts.

By adopting a comprehensive development plan embodying large-scale agricultural diversification and the establishment of simple agriculturally based processing and manufacturing industries, the three cooperative estates could have become the cornerstone of an integrated program of self-reliant agricultural development in Jamaica. This would have helped Jamaica escape the snare of ever increasing debt represented by loans from the International Monetary Fund and the World Bank.

The sugar workers' cooperatives were prevented from reaching their potential as a vehicle for self-reliant development, however, by the same forces that limited the PNP government to moderate reforms. Lacking was any significant change in the class relations inherited from the days of colonialism. As Fals-Borda et al. point out:

> The introduction of cooperatives into local social systems that are already strongly structured along hierarchical lines...often has not brought about ...much reform...New leaders...are quickly co-opted. In some cases, cooperatives...are established only by means of that same local patronage that both social reformism and more comprehensive approaches aim to overthrow (16).

A comprehensive restructuring of the three large sugar estates with full implementation of workers' control would have necessitated curtailing the power of the staff and reducing their numbers (17). Moreover, staff salaries and benefits should have been frozen, with bonuses awarded only when the co-ops were earning a profit. Undoubtedly, such measures would have led to confrontation between members and staff, but in Jamaica's political climate of the mid-1970's the members might well have prevailed.

The entire severance issue could have been avoided if the government had provided equity financing for the co-ops, or had insisted that the members' severance money which was used to purchase the farm assets be treated as an investment refundable as an annuity on retirement, rather than as a loan. Reducing the numbers and influence of the staff and funding the purchase of the standing cane and equipment on the farms with equity instead of debt capital could have resulted in the savings of millions of dollars. A portion of these savings could have gone to reduce costs, and the other portion (as much as J$1 million per year) could have been allocated to cover the capital costs of promoting self-reliant agricultural and agro-industrial development on the farms. With reduced costs, more of the co-ops would have been able to earn profits. Further, if the members had invested their severance money as shares instead of making it a loan, the cooperatives would have avoided a major source of frustration, enabling them to maintain the high initial morale of their members. This would certainly have deprived their opponents of one of their strongest weapons.

Cooperatives in the Context of the Wider Society

What is the "fit" between production cooperatives and the wider sociopolitical system of which they are a part? Is there any one best system within which they are most likely to flourish?

Such cooperatives would probably be most successful in the context of a system that stresses self-reliance and democratic control. Such a system can best be established and maintained where the government is controlled and led by educated and informed representatives of industrial workers and agricultural laborers. This was attempted by the Chinese Communist Party during the 1950's and 1960's, but nowhere in the Third World has such a system been fully implemented.

A democratic socialist society could be organized on the basis of workers cooperatives. The means of production, publicly owned, could consist of a large network of cooperatives organized into area and regional federations whose representatives would take part in a national planning process. In such a system, the cooperative sector would be dominant, though there would be room for small private enterprise and for government administration of certain "natural" monopolies. This is similar to the Yugoslav model of an economy based upon self-management. A key problem for cooperatives within such a setting is how to prevent domination by an oligarchy of "expert" staff over the policy-making boards elected by the membership. Workers' cooperatives can also exist within state socialist economies. But in those situations, they may degenerate even more readily into top-down organizations, run by state-appointed administrators, where democratic control from below is used for window dressing.

Workers' cooperatives can also exist within a capitalist economy, although in the absence of a wider political movement or a government committed to advancing workers' control, such cooperatives usually remain isolated enterprises with little overall economic and political impact. The most successful example of workers' cooperatives in a capitalist country is the network of over 60 industrial cooperatives in the Basque region of Spain near Mondragon that provides employment for more than 20,000 persons. In Mondragon, workers have succeeded in establishing a cooperative economic sector, based in part on internal funding through their own credit union, the Caja Laboral Popular. The entrepreneurial department of the Caja aids in the establishment of new cooperatives by providing feasibility studies, technical assistance, and loans to groups of workers (18).

In Jamaica, the major factors working in favor of the sugar workers' cooperatives' success were the existence of a somewhat favorable political climate, with a government officially committed to their support, and the availability of a technical advisory and catalytic group, the Social Action Centre, which was willing and able to organize a grass-roots cooperative movement. Working against the cooperatives was the fact that they inherited estates that had been allowed to run down through lack of investment. The sugar workers' co-ops took over farms that were marginally viable at best, during a period of general decline in the country's sugar industry. At the same time, the Jamaican co-ops were held back by the ambivalence of the government, which resulted at least partially from the class composition of the civil servants and the leadership of the PNP (19). Few structural changes were made in the external dependent relationships or in the internal political hierarchies, and the co-ops were slowly choked out of existence.

The JLP government (whose support also includes upper- and middle-class professionals and businessmen, as well as affluent farmers) proved itself no friend of the cooperatives. The action of the JLP government in disbanding the Jamaican sugar workers' cooperatives a year after taking office illustrates the way in

which the international and national political structures in neo-colonial societies such as Jamaica hinder
cooperative development.

1. Hazel Henderson, "Rethinking the Economics of World Trade," _Rain_ 7:7, May 1981, p. 17.

2. Michael Manley, _Jamaica: Struggle in the Periphery_ (Third World Media Ltd., 1982).

3. World Bank, _Staff Appraisal Report. Sugar Rehabilitation Project, Jamaica_, January 19, 1978.

4. Jamaica was paying $107 million a year interest on its external public debt in 1980. This represented 13 percent of its export income. _World Development Report_ (Oxford University Press, 1982), p. 134.

5. Manley, _op cit._, pp. 115-117.

6. Former CIA agent Philip Agee came to Jamaica in September 1976 and warned of CIA involvement in destabilization efforts. He listed the names of United States Embassy and Agency for International Development staff in Jamaica who were known CIA agents.

7. For a description of this destabilization effort, see Manley, _op. cit._, especially Chapter 9 and the appendix.

8. The historical record shows a clear pattern of American military intervention against progressive movements in the Caribbean--witness the abortive Bay of Pigs invasion of Cuba in 1960, the occupation of the Dominican Republic by American marines in 1965 to prevent the re-installation of PRD leader Juan Bosch, and the 1983 invasion of Grenada.

9. Henderson, _op. cit_.

10. An example of self-reliance was the system of 70,000 communes established by the Chinese Communists after their military victory in 1949. The communes were based on Mao Tse Tung's philosophy of "regeneration through our own efforts." See Johan Galtung Peter O'Brien and Roy Preiswerk, eds. _Self Reliance: A Strategy for Development_ (Institute for Development Studies, 1980)

11. _Ibid_.

12. See George Beckford, Norman Girvan, Louis Lindsay and Michael Witter, The People's Plan for Socialist Transformation, unpublished PNP Cabinet document. The four authors were social scientists mainly affiliated with the University of the West Indies. The decision not to proceed with such a plan for national self-reliance was part of the PNP's general retreat to the right that included the decision to apply to the IMF for a loan and the ouster of leftist Party Secretary D. K. Duncan.

13. Joseph Collins, What Difference Could a Revolution Make? Food and Farming in the New Nicaragua. (Institute for Food and Development Policy, 1982), p. 111.

14. Assuming three crops per year, and including the labor of watchmen to guard against crop theft, and labor for retail sales, both red beans and fish ponds could contribute several times as many jobs per acre as cane. If each of the 23 farms had devoted only a small fraction of their 1500 acres to these two crops, say 10 acres to fish and 20 acres to beans, collectively they could have produced over 1 1/3 million pounds of fish and more than 400,000 quarts of beans per year, adding significantly to the country's food supply and generating a cash income for the cooperatives.

15. See J.M. Paturau, Byproducts of the Sugar Cane Industry (Elsevier Publishing Co., 1969).

16. Orlando Fals-Borda, Raymond Apthorpe and Inyatullah," The Crisis of Rural Cooperatives: Problems in Africa, Asia and Latin America," in June Nash et al., eds. Popular Participation in Social Change: Cooperatives, Collectives and Nationalized Industry (Mouton Publ., 1976), p. 447.

17. The numbers of staff could have been cut, for example, by retaining only one manager for each farm, hiring one progressive organizer/educator for each, and requiring that one of the sugar workers be promoted to a staff position as assistant to the manager, for a total of three employees per farm.

18. Ana Gutierrez Johnson and William Foote Whyte, "The Mondragon System of Worker Production Cooperatives" in Frank Lindenfeld and Joyce Rothschild-Whitt, eds. Workplace Democracy and Social Change (Porter Sargent, 1982); and Ana Gutierrez Johnson "The Mondragon Model of Cooperative Enterprise," Changing Work, 1:1, pp. 35-41.

19. Perhaps because it has been ideologically linked with the Soviet and Cuban systems, the small Workers Party of Jamaica has had only limited appeal in spite of its close identification with the interests of the working class.

EPILOGUE

It is back to Big Man control again.
(Cooperator)

On Tuesday, November 3, 1981, the Minister of Agriculture, Percival Broderick, announced that the sugar cooperatives at Frome, Monymusk and Bernard Lodge were to be dismantled and taken over by the government. He said that the decision was based on a report from the Registrar of Cooperatives and on the view that the cooperatives were financially bankrupt. The announcement came as a surprise to most of the co-op members:

> I never realized that they (the JLP government) would take it (the co-op) away. I never really thought so. Finally it really happened. (Ex-co-op Chairperson and PNP member.)

> I believed that the co-op would run the same way (after the election). You see I never expected that it would be dropped. Well, it was a heart-rending tune, because I never expected that it was going to work that way. (Ex-Education Committee member and JLP supporter.)

> I tell you I was expecting restructuring; I wasn't expecting it to be abolished. I felt bad when I heard it on the radio. (Ex-Education Committee Chairperson and PNP supporter).

The bitterness was all the more pronounced because the JLP government, headed by Edward P. Seaga, had in numerous announcements reassured the cooperators of its support for the sugar cooperatives. The pre-election JLP Manifesto included the following statement:

> With respect to the sugar cooperatives it needs to be made clear that they are consistent with JLP policy; however, they need to be strengthened and the JLP will allocate the necessary funds for the technical assistance which is

185

> needed to improve efficiency in the
> co-op.

After the election victory, various government officials continued to publicly express their support for
the cooperatives. In January of 1981, the Parliamentary Secretary in the Ministry of Agriculture, Astil
Sangster, declared that the new government was fully
committed to the cooperatives. He was more ambiguous
when addressing cooperators at Frome about the severance pay issue; promising the members their severance
money and continued work in the co-op, he also suggested that the cooperators couldn't have their cake
and eat it, too (i.e., the members couldn't get their
deposit back and have the co-op, too). In April 1981,
the Parliamentary Secretary in the Ministry of Youth
and Community Development, Kingsley Sangster, and the
Permanent Secretary in the same ministry, Cedric
McCulloch, both came out in support of the cooperatives. All through the year, "restructuring" was
promised by various government officials as the remedy
for the financially troubled sugar co-ops.

At the same time, it was clear that at least some
government officials were looking for ways to destroy
the co-ops. A "restructuring" proposal was requested
by the government from Tate and Lyle Technical Services Ltd., which included the requirement that the
cooperatives be transferred to the National Sugar
Company before the start of the 1982 crop. When these
proposals were leaked to the press in March 1981,
Agriculture Minister Broderick declared that the
government opposed the plan. Workers' Time notes that
this was before the end of the 1981 crop and that the
Minister in all likelihood feared that the co-op
workers would go on strike if the government declared
its real intent at that time (1).

In the meantime, the severance deposit issue
again became a political football, as had been the
case so often in the past. When Astil Sangster went
to Bernard Lodge to discuss the matter, the members
there made it very clear that they did not intend to
abandon their cooperative and did not want their
deposit back. Lists were circulated on all three
estates where those members who wanted their deposit
to be returned signed their names. At Bernard Lodge
only 8 percent of the members signed up; at Monymusk
40 percent signed and at Frome 90 percent added their

186

names to the list. At a later meeting between the SIA chairman, the Registrar of Cooperatives and the members of the USWCC Central Board, it became clear to the board members that the government had assumed that if all the cooperators signed up for the deposit, it would be taken as a sign that the members didn't want to keep their co-op. The Central Board members strongly refuted this and pointed out that the members had been told that they could have their severance money _and_ the co-op, too. It was then agreed that a survey was to be carried out on the farms to find out what the members really wanted.

At Frome, the Project Managers and other staff immediately told the cooperators that the survey was a trick; if they answered the questions, they would not get their severance deposit back. This caused such a mighty upheaval that the survey could not be carried out there. However, at Monymusk and Bernard Lodge the survey was conducted without major problems and the message was clear: the majority of the cooperators did _not_ want to give up their cooperatives. Shortly after these events, the members of all ten farms at Frome went on strike demanding to know something definite about their severance money. Astil Sangster returned to Frome where he addressed the members just five days before the Parish Council elections.

Sangster pointed out what the JLP government had done for the people in its first one-hundred days in office; when some members started protesting against his speech, which was clearly designed to make political mileage for the JLP, he told the crowd that he had requested but had not yet received the list of names of those who wanted their deposit refunded. The Frome Chief Executive replied that the list had been sent to the General Secretary of the co-op, E.B. Thompson. Conveniently ignoring the reply, Sangster claimed to have heard nothing about the survey yet accused the education team of using the survey to delay matters. In his speech, Sangster told the cooperators that they would get their checks in two weeks. As the people started to shout for joy, he said that in three weeks they would know when they would get their checks, and then changed his wording again to say that in a few weeks time they would hear about the checks.

A few weeks prior to his speech at Frome, Astil Sangster had told two of the co-op leaders there that

he had received the list of names from Frome. Because
he later told the Frome cooperators in his speech that
he had received no list, he was apparently trying to
discredit the co-op leadership. One of the leaders
wrote to us in March 1981:

> Generally speaking, the outlook of the
> co-op is very dim; it is clear to me
> that the government has decided to
> destroy the co-op.

The cooperatives were slowly being strangled to
death. The severance deposit was not returned, the
after-crop bonus payment, payment of a retroactive
wage increase, of vacation and sick-leave pay, and
interest on the deposit were not forthcoming on the
dates when they had normally been paid. Such delays
had occurred numerous times before, but the Sugar
Industry Authority had always "found" some money for
the payments when the members threatened or actually
went on strike. This time, however, the members and
the co-op leaders were immobilized, waiting for some
definite action, suspended by uncertainty and the
government's promises that restructuring was to begin
soon. Morale among the members was at an all-time
low.

In the summer of 1981, the members, who had
normally been paid early Friday afternoon, were not
getting their pay until late Friday evening or Saturday morning. A leader at Frome commented:

> When people cannot get their money,
> they blame everything entirely on the
> co-op, and this strategy is succeeding.

New dates were continuously being given by government
officials for when the bonus and other payments were
to be made. In the midst of the crisis, the annual
general meetings of the primary cooperatives were held
at Frome between July 14 and 29. The payments had
been promised by the central co-op staff for July 24
and 30. The meetings were dominated by the burning
question of whether the money would actually be paid
this time. The meetings at Georges Plain and Belle
Isle erupted into chaos over the issue. In the
meantime, Central Board members were asking the SIA to
make the money available for the payments. SIA
Chairman Noel Rennie refused. On July 24 and 30, the

cooperators had to be once again told by their leaders that no money was forthcoming.

What added to the already volatile situation was the fact that the August 8 Independence Day was near, and the members had counted on the extra money to be able to celebrate as they had in previous years. The cooperators were so upset that they retaliated by going on strike. No work or education was carried out on any of the ten farms at Frome; there was a complete shut down. On July 30, some three hundred cooperators from Mint, Frome, Belle Isle, and Albany farms stormed the Frome office demanding their money. Matthias Brown spoke to them and tried to explain what was really taking place. The people listened, and many started to go home. But one cooperator from Tractor and Transport refused to be appeased; he told the remaining crowd that it is "fool Matthias fooling them" and that Matthias and General Secretary E. B. Thompson had stolen the money and couldn't find it to pay them now. Matthias and the cooperator ended up in a fist fight. One of the literacy teachers commented on this sad state of affairs:

> What the government is doing is demoralizing the people and getting them frustrated so that they smash themselves.

Amidst the confusion and uncertainty, the co-ops undertook a campaign for survival. The members of Bernard Lodge took the lead. As early as December 1980, the Bernard Lodge Estate Board presented information to the new government which showed how the sugar cooperatives as a group could move toward viability. There was no response from the government to this report. On March 20 and April 10, letters were sent to Prime Minister Seaga by the same board, requesting a meeting with him to discuss the future of the cooperatives and the plans which the cooperators themselves had for restructuring their organization. In the letters, it was noted that even though the government's plans were soon to be announced, the people who would be affected by these plans the most, the workers, had not been consulted. Bernard Lodge received no reply from the Prime Minister. The Bernard Lodge Estate Board wrote again in July suggesting a meeting with a government representative where they could get a hearing to present their updated plan for restructuring the cooperatives.

In late August, a government inquiry administered by the Registrar of Cooperatives was held, ostensibly to determine what the members felt should be done about the cooperatives. "Restructuring" was still the government's officially stated intent. But it was soon clear to most people involved that the sole inquirer, Anthony Drummond, was mainly interested in hearing the opinions of those cooperators and staff who opposed the cooperative. What he actually heard, however, was a different story. Cooperator after cooperator, even at Frome, stood up and defended the co-op, listing as main problems excessive and ineffective staff, high overhead costs, and lack of financing. According to the Estate Boards of Frome and Monymusk, Drummond's conduct was so obviously biased that the two boards found it necessary to lodge formal complaints with the Registrar of Cooperatives. The letter from Frome charged that Drummond "told the cooperators who testified at the enquiry that he didn't believe them when they spoke of mismanagement by the technical staff" and "when some cooperators spoke against their cooperatives and themselves, he openly praised them, shook their hands and told them that was what he wanted to hear." Both the Frome and Monymusk Estate Boards complained that the inquirer insulted some of the cooperators, and that he tried to confuse presentations which he obviously didn't agree with. The Monymusk Board also complained that the inquirer gave the impression that the losses incurred by the cooperatives were caused by misappropriation, and that the estate and farm committee Chairpersons were expected to testify in open hearings while staff members were allowed to give their testimony behind closed doors (3).

In the meantime, the cooperators were still waiting for their payments. In August, the Sugar Industry Authority officials said that the members would hear about their money in September, but no money was paid. Finally, some of the members at Bernard Lodge had had enough; they went to the SIA head office in Kingston to see the Chairman, Noel Rennie, and demanded their bonus payment. The money was found, and all the cooperators were paid their after-crop bonus shortly thereafter.

In early November 1981, after a year of financial
hardship, sagging morale and debilitating uncertainty
about the future, the co-ops were brought to an abrupt
end. The Seaga government declared the cooperatives
bankrupt. The cultivation of the cane lands at Frome,
Monymusk and Bernard Lodge was to be managed directly
by the Jamaican government through the state-owned
National Sugar Company.

Ironically, the government acted illegally in the
manner in which the cooperatives were dissolved. The
cooperatives have claimed that the events leading up
to the dissolution of the co-ops and the pronouncements by Minister of Agriculture Broderick clearly
indicate that it was the government's decision to end
the cooperatives, when in fact only the Registrar of
Cooperatives had the legal authority to do so. The
Agriculture Minister implied that he acted on the
recommendation of the Registrar, but the decision was
taken before the government had received a full report
from Drummond. Even so, the decision to dissolve the
co-ops was made against the preliminary recommendation
of the inquirer that three farms should continue under
cooperative ownership and that further investigation
was required before making a decision about the fate
of the other farms. In addition, according to cooperative law, written notice of termination of registra-
tion must be given two months before termination to
allow for appeal. The government did not wait two
months, but took control immediately after the announcement. Nine farms did appeal the decision, but
instead of allowing those farms to continue as cooperatives until the appeals process was exhausted, the
government immediately seized the assets of all 23
farms and placed them under National Sugar Company
management.

The government deliberately delayed the appeals
process. Although the government officials had made
their decision in November 1981, they did not release
the preliminary report of Drummond's inquiry until the
spring of 1982 in response to pressure from the
attorneys filing the appeals for the nine farms (4).
Not until then did the cooperatives learn that the
inquirer had in fact recommended that Salt Pond, March
Pen and Barham be given the required help and be
allowed to continue the cooperative experiment, or
that he recommended further studies to determine

whether there should be a return to the cooperative system for all the farms on the three estates (5).

Many months later the government finally appointed a three-member Tribunal to hear the appeals. But it was not until August 1983 that the Tribunal heard arguments for the cooperatives appealing the case. Attorneys for the cooperatives presented arguments and data showing why they should be allowed to continue. The record of March Pen, for example, was particularly outstanding. That farm earned a profit during three of the five years it was under workers' control. It achieved more than a J$200,000 profit in 1981, its last year as a cooperative (6). The attorneys further pointed out that at Monymusk, the government never implemented any of the special measures necessary for the revival of that estate, which were spelled out in the second report of the Prime Minister's Committee on Cooperative Development in July 1975. In areas that were under the cooperators' control, the Monymusk farms nevertheless managed to cut costs. The argument for Springfield, for example, was that the cooperative had outpaced similar irrigated cane farms in Clarendon by 1980, with total production costs of J$32 per ton compared with Clarendon farmers' costs of $41 per ton.

> Although Springfield has sustained accumulated losses, its performance was better in every category than the (other) local cane producers, and therefore, government should not have closed (it)...Of course, Springfield was in a bankrupt position in 1981. It was bankrupt when it started as is recognized the whole of Vere cane production was bankrupt. Remedies were suggested in 1976, but nothing was done. Over the years, Springfield Cooperative was coping better than the others at Vere (7).

The arguments fell on deaf ears. All three members of the Tribunal were conservatives, and their decision not to reinstate the cooperatives was a foregone conclusion. Not surprisingly, the Tribunal report released by the government in February 1984 rejected the appeals, stating that the re-establishment of the cooperatives "would not serve any useful purpose" (8).

In November 1981, a few days after the government had announced the dissolution of the cooperatives, members of retirement age began receiving notice that they were not to return to work, and were finally refunded their severance deposits (9). Within the next few months, about 1200 members were laid off. All Central Board members were among those fired; only one was later rehired by the National Sugar Company. The education program was terminated immediately, even before the IAF grant money had been used up, and all education staff members were dismissed. Many terminations were clearly political in nature, although Prime Minister Seaga had declared that no victimization of political opponents would take place after the elections. Two of the staff fired at Frome, for example, had been cooperators who as accounting clerks crossed the picket line to help the members with the payroll during the staff strike in 1981. The most vocal of the co-op's leaders, Matthias Brown, was told that he would have no chance of getting a job with National Sugar Company. He claims that Astil Sangster told him that he wanted to see Matthias "crawl on his belly." In the previous year, Matthias had been accused of being a "communist," and he had also been threatened with arrest in August -- just before the dissolution of the co-op was to take place -- on charges of carrying guns to one of the Frome farms before the 1980 elections. He was finally arrested on those charges in July 1982, almost two years after the alleged incident, just before he was about to leave for Canada. He had been granted a fellowship by the Inter-American Foundation for a six-month program in Social Development at the Coady International Institute of St. Francis Xavier University, Nova Scotia, Canada. While in jail, he was beaten so badly by a guard that he required hospital treatment. When the trial was to begin in September of 1982, none of the prosecution witnesses showed up, and the trial was postponed until February 1983. Rather than dismissing the charges, the trial was again put off several more times for the lack of prosecution witnesses until the case was finally thrown out a year and a half later.

For those who remained on the farms, conditions changed for the worse. Overtime work was eliminated; some task-work rates were lowered, and sick leave was

193

reduced from fourteen days to five. Even small violations of work rules, such as tardiness, were punished by the loss of work (and thus pay) for one or more days. A worker could no longer demand work as his or her right and had to accept whatever work was given no matter how objectionable. No Trespass signs emerged all over the estates prohibiting people from tying their cows or goats on National Sugar Company land. Heavy fines were imposed on anyone caught with animals on intervals and outskirts land, even if the cane was not damaged. No more funeral grants were paid, and no assistance was available to sugar workers or their families for making burial arrangements. The Member Service Officers were fired, and the office itself was abolished. There was now no one to turn to for help with housing and benefit applications, for filling in tax returns, for clarifying payroll discrepancies, for transportation to hospitals or funerals, or for information about pay raises, education scholarships, seminars or co-op business matters. The National Sugar Company also seized the special loan funds of the cooperatives which had been used to provide loans to needy members. The sugar workers again depended solely upon the busha for the above services, assuming that they found favor with him, of course.

Knowledge was again the privilege of managers only. All consultations with the workers or their leaders about work schedules, budgets and production plans ceased. The sugar workers no longer had the opportunity to learn on the job, since the education program was terminated immediately after the government take-over. The director of the co-op education program was hired by the National Sugar Company to set up another program, but at the writing of this book there has been no sign of such a program and most workers believe that there will never be one. With the co-op education program gone, the workers also lost the opportunity for travel and education abroad, for travel inside Jamaica, for meeting new and different people, and for producing their own cultural events as well as attending those of others. Their leaders no longer had direct access to high government officials, granting agencies and Jamaican and foreign guests interested in cooperative development. They could no longer make their own plans for their business.

Because of their inability to find employment, former leaders were reduced to a position of powerlessness. Their isolation from the estates and from each other because of lack of transportation, effectively cut them off from the struggle in the cane fields, and, at least temporarily, immobilized them. Without their leaders, the workers who continued to cultivate the sugar cane felt voiceless and powerless. Although the JLP government paid back all the former co-op members their severance deposit in December 1981, there was a keen sense of loss even among those who before had allowed the non-payment of the severance deposit to cloud the issues and weaken their support for the co-op:

> The cow never knows the use of her tail until she loses it. They have been bawling that they want the severance deposit to be paid, how long can that carry them? You get one or two-thousand dollars and in two or three months you finish it and you are penniless. They miss the cooperatives now. They never felt that they would really get back their deposit. Now they have gotten it, the co-op is mashed up and they don't have the money and now they want back the co-op. (Ex-Chairman at Frome)

A small minority were glad to see the co-op destroyed, especially those workers who had continued to fight against their own leaders to curry favor with the busha. Others had simply been afraid to openly take sides, anticipating changes and wanting to protect themselves for the time when the Big Man would be back in full control again. The Big Man was back, but not everything was quite the same as it was before the co-op. At Frome, where the sugar workers had some other livelihood to fall back on, the workers refused to submit totally to the new regime. If the work was unacceptable, i.e., a task such as weeding was so hard that too little work could be done to earn a reasonable wage for the day, a worker would refuse and go home rather than do the work. At Monymusk and Bernard Lodge, this could not be done as readily because there were practically no alternative sources of income. Instead, there was a strong sense of unity:

You know what I see now is that the
workers have unity with one another.
Yes, they have a unity between themselves. They are not afraid now. They
have a certain thing in them that they
are not afraid to tell the busha or the
bookkeeper or the headman what they
think. In the past days they couldn't
do it because they would get victim-
ized. But now they just have that urge
in them from the cooperative movement.
And they just don't forget it. (Norma
Brown, Exeter farm, Monymusk)

By fall 1983, the crisis in the government-owned
sugar industry came to a head. Sugar production for
Jamaica fell more than 100,000 tons short of the
government's projected goal of over 300,000 tons. The
National Sugar Company announced that it was closing
its seven sugar factories for at least two months. In
consequence, 11,000 factory and field workers were
temporarily laid off. At the end of October, Agriculture Minister Broderick announced that over 1,000 of
these laid-off workers would not be called back to
work.

In accordance with its policy of converting
government-owned enterprises back into private hands,
the Seaga government had been searching diligently
since its first year in office for new owners or
managers for the ailing cane estates and sugar factories. In July 1984, Agriculture Minister Broderick
confirmed the long-rumored return of Tate and Lyle,
whose subsidiary WISCO had been the former owner of
the Frome and Monymusk estates. Tate and Lyle was to
begin a ten-year management contract in January of
1985, involving the management of both factory and
field operations at Frome, Monymusk and Bernard Lodge.
Thus the same company which had sold the sugar estates
some fifteen years earlier because they were unprofitable is now being paid by the Jamaican government J$7
million for the first year alone to administer these
estates. A new company, Jamaica Sugar Holdings, is to
replace the National Sugar Company as holder of the
lease on the three factory-estates. Three of the
seven company directors are to be appointed by Tate
and Lyle (10).

Meanwhile, the Jamaican economy was undergoing a severe crisis. By 1983, following two years of moderate economic growth sustained by massive borrowing and a limited increase in foreign investment, it was clear that Seaga's revival of the industrialization-by-invitation development model had again failed to raise the living standards of the majority of Jamaicans. At the end of 1984, official unemployment stood at over 30 percent with more lay-offs expected in the public sector in 1985; inflation for 1984 was estimated at 37 percent; basic food prices and utility rates rose sharply after the removal of government subsidies; total export earnings fell to 65 percent of 1980 levels while a flood of imports hurt many domestic industries and aggravated the shortage of foreign exchange; the Jamaican dollar was devalued numerous times from J$1.78 to US$1.00 in 1980 to J$4.97 to US$1.00 in January 1985; and the external debt almost doubled between 1980 and 1984. Austerity measures imposed by the International Monetary Fund requiring lay-offs, the removal of government subsidies and the devaluation of the Jamaican dollar not only hurt the average Jamaican worker and consumer but also undermined local businesses. The dissatisfaction with Seaga's economic policies erupted in massive riots in January 1985 in response to the government's announcement of a 20-percent gasoline price hike. Roadblocks of burning tires, old cars, garbage and other debris brought the island to a standstill. Schools were closed, airports shut down and almost all transportation was halted.

When the dissolution of the cooperatives was announced by the JLP-controlled government in the fall of 1981, it may have seemed that the workers' struggle was ultimately lost. We are convinced that the moment represented only a temporary setback. There is no doubt that the large-scale lay-offs and especially the firing of so many of the outstanding leaders of the sugar workers greatly weakened the workers' ability to struggle for a better life for themselves and their families. But in many of those who remained in the cane fields there was a vastly increased consciousness of what was possible. Their short-lived experience of cooperative ownership and control gave them a new perspective on democracy, a perspective which holds that no society is truly democratic unless those who produce control the means of production. This realization certainly helped the Jamaican sugar workers to forge new strategies and tactics for the struggles that lay ahead. Workers' committees were soon organized on all three estates, providing the first new links among the workers since their co-ops were abolished. Opposition to the government's actions focused on the appeals demanding reinstatement of the nine cooperatives, the claims of the former co-op members to notice and redundancy pay (11) and to just compensation for the assets seized by the National Sugar Company when the co-ops were terminated.

In March 1984, thousands of sugar workers at Monymusk went on strike to demand 14 weeks' pay in lieu of notice (of dismissal). Workers' committees at Monymusk and Bernard Lodge demonstrated together in front of the two radio stations in Kingston to voice their demand for the 14 week/severance payment and to oppose price increases and the closing of sugar factories. Under pressure, the government promised an inquiry into the matter, which finally got under way in April. Almost nine months later the Board of Enquiry finally determined that the government was not legally responsible for such additional severance payments and instead urged the liquidators of the co-ops to give these claims high priority in the liquidation of the co-ops' assets. The Board of Enquiry also noted that liquidators had not been appointed for all farms (four years after the government had declared the co-ops bankrupt!) and urged that: "Where there are no liquidators appointed then this should be done immediately." The government's obvious lack of concern for the rights of the former cooperators compelled all 140 remaining workers at Frome's Barham farm (one of the three former pilot co-ops) to seize control over farm equipment, to occupy the farm office and to briefly detain the busha as a protest against the National Sugar Company seizure of their assets when the co-ops were disbanded. For nine weeks the Barham workers kept watch over their equipment and sent delegations to Kingston to pressure the Registrar of Cooperatives to meet with them and to negotiate their demands. Through these actions, they won the return of the funds they had deposited with the cooperatives that had been illegally impounded by the company. A liquidator was finally appointed to assess the value of Barham's assets and to determine proper compensation. Meanwhile other sugar workers at Frome invaded the factory compound, detained two National Sugar Company officials, and had them secure a promise for payment of the after-crop bonus the next day from the company headquarters in Kingston.

The struggle in the sugar fields continues. The sugar cooperatives are gone for the moment, but Father Joe Owens' vision which compelled him to begin organizing in the cane fields of Monymusk, remains:

> Just as an earthquake cannot strike any part of the earth without sending its reverberations throughout the planet, so this advance toward worker control of industry cannot occur without profoundly affecting the whole Jamaican social order. Every economic force, every social position, every political event will be affected, and the workers will realize that their task is not simply controlling a farm, or an estate, or even an industry, but the whole society. They will recognize that the day has passed when a small elite could exploit and control the masses -- the day has finally dawned when the working people, the powerful heart of the nation, become dynamic agents in the creation of a new society, a new economy, a new heaven and a new earth.

1. Workers' Time, Vol. 9 (7-8), August-September 1983, pp. 3-4.

2. Personal communication from two co-op members present at the meeting.

3. Workers' Time, Vol. 6 (8-10), 1981.

4. Barham, Georges Plain and Mint at Frome; March Pen, Salt Pond and Windsor Park at Bernard Lodge; and Hillside, Greenwich and Springfield at Monymusk.

5. Workers' Time, Vol. 7 (4-5), May-June 1982.

6. "Brief History of Management Practice," p. 5. Social Action Centre brief used by the co-op attorneys.

7. "Performance of Springfield Sugar Workers' Cooperative," p. 3 of Social Action Centre brief. Vere refers to the region in which the Monymusk estate is located.

8. Workers' Time, Vol. 10 (1), February 1984.

9. Some older workers had wanted to retire before, but could not because they were told there was no money with which to pay their severance deposit.

10. Workers' Time, Vol. 10 (10), November 1984.

11. These severance claims stemmed from the changeover from cooperative to government ownership of the estates. They were unrelated to the previously discussed severance payments which the cooperators had deposited as loans to the co-ops and which had been paid back shortly after the co-ops were abolished.

BIBLIOGRAPHY

Beckford, George, Norman Girvan, Louis Lindsey and Michael Witter, The People's Plan for Socialist Transformation, Unpublished PNP Cabinet document.

Collins, Joseph, What Difference Could a Revolution Make? Food and Farming in the New Nicaragua. (Institute for Food and Development Policy, 1982).

Craton, Michael, Sinews of Empire. A Short History of British Slavery. (Anchor Books, 1974).

Fals-Borda, Orlando, Raymond Apthorpe and Inyatullah, eds., "The Crisis of Rural Cooperatives: Problems in Africa, Asia and Latin America," in June Nash et al., eds., Popular Participation in Social Change: Cooperatives, Collectives and Nationalized Industry. (Mouton Publ., 1976).

Feuer, Carl, Jamaica and Sugar Workers' Cooperatives: The Politics of Reform. Ph.D. Dissertation, Cornell University, 1983.

Feuer, Carl, "The Internal Political Economy of Democratic Reform: Sugar Workers' Cooperatives in Jamaica." Paper presented at the 37th Annual Conference of the New York State Political Science Association in New York, April 9, 1983.

Feuer, Carl, Jamaica and the Sugar Worker Cooperatives. The Politics of Reform. (Westview, 1984).

Galtung, Johan, Peter O'Brien and Roy Preiswerk, eds. Self Reliance: A Strategy For Development. (Institute for Development Studies, 1980).

Girling, Robert and Sherry Keith, Jamaica's Employment Crisis: A Political-Economic Evaluation of the Jamaican Special Employment Program. (Center for Economic Studies, Palo Alto, 1977).

Gutiérrez Johnson, Ana and William Foote Whyte, "The Mondragón System of Worker Production Cooperatives," in Frank Lindenfeld and Joyce Rothschild-Whitt, eds., Workplace Democracy and Social Change. (Porter Sargent, 1982).

Gutiérrez Johnson, Ana, "The Mondragón Model of Cooperative Enterprise." Changing Work, 1(1):35-41, 1984.

Hamid, Idris, ed., The World of Sugar Workers. (Caribbean Ecumenical Programme, Trinidad, 1978).

Henderson, Hazel, "Rethinking the Economics of World Trade," Rain Vol. 7(7), 1981.

International Sugar Organization Yearbook, 1981.

Knight, Franklin, The Caribbean. The Genesis of a Fragmented Nationalism. (Oxford University Press, 1978).

Levy, Horace, "What's Wrong with the Sugar Co-ops?" Public Opinion, February 24, 1978.

Manley, Michael, A Voice at the Workplace. (Andre Deutch, 1975).

Manley, Michael, Jamaica: Struggle in the Periphery. (Third World Media Ltd., 1982).

Mays, Jeb, ed., Jamaica: Caribbean Challenge. (EPICA Task Force, 1979).

Patterson, Orlando, The Sociology of Slavery. (McGibbon and Kee, 1967).

Paturau, J. M. Byproducts of the Sugar Cane Industry. (Elsevier Publishing Co., 1969).

Phillips, James, "Renovation of the International Economic Order: Trilateralism, the IMF and Jamaica," in Holly Sklar, ed., Trilateralism, (South End Press, 1980).

Phillips, Peter, "Jamaican elites: 1938 to Present," in Carl Stone, and Aggrey Brown, eds., Essays on Power and Change in Jamaica. (Jamaica Publishing House, 1977).

Richards, Vincent A. and Alan N. Williams, "Some Institutional and Economic Aspects of the Jamaican Sugar Cooperatives." Paper presented for Association for Caribbean Transformation, April 1981.

Social Action Centre, "Brief History of Management Practice" and "Performance of Springfield Sugar Workers' Cooperative." Briefs prepared in 1983.

Stone, Carl, "An Appraisal of the Cooperative Process in the Jamaican Sugar Industry," Social and Economic Studies, Vol. 27(1), 1978.

Stone, Carl, Democracy and Clientelism in Jamaica. (Transaction Books, 1980).

Sugar World, Vol. 3(3,5), 1980.

United Sugar Workers' Cooperative Council, "Guidelines for Committee Members of Sugar Worker Cooperatives," and "Management and Development of Sugar Workers' Cooperatives," 1976.

United Sugar Workers' Cooperative Council, Press Release, March 27, 1979.

United Sugar Workers' Cooperative Council, Minutes of the Central Board and Central Office records.

Von Freyhold, Michaela, Ujamaa Villages in Tanzania. (Monthly Review Press, 1979).

Williams, Eric, Capitalism and Slavery. (Capricorn Books, 1966).

World Bank, Staff Appraisal Report. Sugar Rehabilitation Project. Jamaica. January 19, 1978.

World Development Report 1982. (Oxford University Press, 1982).

Workers' Time, 1976-1984.

APPENDIX I

ACRONYMS

BITU - Bustamante Industrial Trade Union

CDC - Cooperative Development Centre

EEC - European Economic Community

FMLCO - Frome Monymusk Land Company

IAF - Inter-American Foundation

IMF - International Monetary Fund

JAMAL - Jamaica Movement for the Advancement of Literacy

JLP - Jamaica Labour Party

MSO - Member Service Officer

NHT - National Housing Trust

NIEO - New International Economic Order

NSC - National Sugar Company

NWU - National Workers' Union

PNP - People's National Party

SAC - Social Action Centre

SIA - Sugar Industry Authority

SIRI - Sugar Industry Research Institute

SWCC - Sugar Workers' Cooperative Council

T&T - Tractor and Transport

USWCC - United Sugar Workers' Cooperative Council

WISCO - West Indies Sugar Company

WPJ - Workers' Party of Jamaica

APPENDIX II

GLOSSARY

BAUXITE   Aluminum ore from which an intermediate product, alumina, is produced. Bauxite provides a majority of Jamaica's foreign exchange income.

BIG MAN   General term used by workers for the executive-managerial class as well as for the wealthy and powerful.

BUSHA   Colloquial term applied to the manager of a cane farm, especially before the co-op days. Renamed Project Manager after the co-ops were established.

BUSTAMANTE INDUSTRIAL TRADE UNION (BITU)
Originally founded by populist leader Alexander Bustamante. Now headed by former JLP Prime Minister Hugh Shearer, it is allied with the JLP. Two thirds of the sugar workers belong to this union.

BUTTERFOOT
Workers hired by the cooperatives to do day labor, who were not co-op members.

CENTRAL BOARD
The 11-member policy-making body of the United Sugar Workers Cooperative Council, the tertiary-level co-op that united the cooperative cane farms on the three estates. It consisted of worker representatives chosen by the three Estate Boards.

COOPERATIVE DEVELOPMENT CENTRE (CDC)
A bureau under the Cooperative Department of the Ministry of Agriculture, established in 1977. It was then headed by Cedric McCulloch.

CROP SEASON
The time during which cane is harvested and the factories are operating, extending from January through June in Jamaica.

DEAD SEASON
> Out-of-crop season (July - December) when the level of activity on the cane farms decreases markedly because no harvesting is done.

DRIBBLE   Pieces of cane cut to about one foot and planted in furrows to grow cane. (The cane from which it is cut is known as seed cane).

DRIVER   Female farm worker who has been promoted to supervisory position.

ESTATE   Large plantation consisting of several cane farms, clustered around a factory.

ESTATE BOARD
> The 11-member policy-making body at each of the three cooperative estates; its members included all chairpersons of the farm Managing Committees.

EUROPEAN ECONOMIC COMMUNITY
> A group of European countries that has been the purchaser of the Jamaican quota of sugar exports at guaranteed prices under the International Sugar Agreement.

FROME MONYMUSK LAND COMPANY (FMLCO)
> Also referred to as the Land Company. Government agency established to oversee the Frome, Monymusk and Bernard Lodge sugar estates purchased from the transnational corporations.

GRABBER   Mechanical loader that grabs piles of cut cane with large pincers and places it on trailers for transport to the factory.

HEADMAN   Male farm worker who has been promoted to supervisory position.

HIGGLER   Small trader who buys wholesale or direct from producers and sells on the streets or in the market.

INTER-AMERICAN FOUNDATION (IAF)
    Liberal foundation whose income derives from
    the United States government. It funded
    cooperative organizing by the Social Action
    Centre and also funded the cooperatives' own
    education program.

INTERNATIONAL MONETARY FUND (IMF)
    An international lending agency to which the
    United States is a major contributor. Its
    primary function is to aid third world
    countries having balance-of-payments prob-
    lems. Its loan conditions usually provide
    for devaluation of the local currency and a
    reduction of government spending for social
    programs.

JAMAICA LABOUR PARTY (JLP)
    Pro-capitalist, and more conservative of the
    two major political parties, with many
    adherents among the sugar workers. Founded
    by Alexander Bustamante, it is currently
    headed by Prime Minister Edward Seaga.

JAMAICA MOVEMENT FOR THE ADVANCEMENT OF LITERACY
(JAMAL)
    Organization promoting adult education.

LABOURITE
    Supporter of the Jamaica Labour Party.

LAND COMPANY
    See Frome Monymusk Land Company.

MANAGING COMMITTEE
    An 11-member policy-making body for each
    cooperative cane farm. This committee
    elected its own officers. It was supposed
    to oversee the farms and provide direction
    to the hired staff.

MEMBER SERVICE OFFICER (MSO)

    New position created by the cooperatives to
    give advice to the Managing Committees and
    to help members regarding their fringe
    benefits. Until the establishment of the
    cooperatives' Education Department, these
    staff members also conducted education
    programs.

NATIONAL HOUSING TRUST (NHT)
> A housing trust fund established by the PNP government to finance housing development. Funded by mandatory contributions from employees and employers.

NATIONAL SUGAR COMPANY (NSC)
> Government-owned corporation which managed the nationalized sugar factories during the cooperative era. After the co-ops were disbanded by the JLP government, the NSC became the caretaker of the cane farms at Frome, Monymusk and Bernard Lodge.

NATIONAL WORKERS' UNION (NWU)
> "Middle of the road" labor union allied with the People's National Party. It has fewer adherents among the sugar workers than the rival BITU but otherwise is quite similar to that union.

NEW INTERNATIONAL ECONOMIC ORDER (NIEO)
> Vision of a changed world trade system wherein third world nations would receive guaranteed higher than world market prices for commodities sold to industrial nations. Former Jamaican Prime Minister Michael Manley has been one of the leading proponents of such a change.

PATOIS
> Local dialect based on English spoken by most Jamaicans; the every day language of the working class.

PEOPLE'S NATIONAL PARTY (PNP)
> One of the two major parties. Proposes a democratic socialist political program. Founded by Norman Manley, father of present head, Michael Manley.

PRIMARY CO-OP
> Refers to each one of the 23 cane farms on the three cooperative sugar estates, and the Tractor and Transport and Irrigation Departments of those estates. The first level of governance of the three-tiered co-op structure.

PROJECT MANAGER
New name for manager of cane farm during the cooperative era. Formerly called busha.

SEVERANCE DEPOSIT
Money lent to the cooperatives by their members, originally for two years, to help finance the original purchase of the cane farm assets. This money represented half of the severance pay received by the sugar workers from their previous employers.

SOCIAL ACTION CENTRE (SAC)
Jesuit-founded organization that mobilized the sugar workers to form cooperatives and provided them with education and technical assistance.

STAND-OVER CANE
Mature cane not reaped at harvest time and left standing in the fields.

SUGAR INDUSTRY AUTHORITY (SIA)
Government agency that purchases all cane and is sole agent for marketing sugar in Jamaica and abroad. It sets prices to be paid farmers and sugar factories.

SUGAR INDUSTRY RESEARCH INSTITUTE (SIRI)
Government sponsored research center funded by the Sugar Industry Authority.

SUGAR WORKERS' COOPERATIVE COUNCIL (SWCC)
Mass organization of sugar workers interested in transforming the three major sugar estates into cooperatives. It was in existence from 1973 to 1975, after which the new co-op organization, the United Sugar Workers Cooperative Council, was formed.

TRACTOR AND TRANSPORT (T&T)
A department of each estate that formed its own primary cooperative. T&T was responsible for cultivating the fields with tractors and for loading and transportation of the cut cane.

UNITED SUGAR WORKERS' COOPERATIVE COUNCIL (USWCC)
      The tertiary-level cooperative that united
      the three secondary level cooperatives at
      Frome, Monymusk and Bernard Lodge. The
      Central Board of the USWCC hired the staff
      executives and had the formal power to set
      overall policy for the co-ops.

WEST INDIES SUGAR COMPANY (WISCO)
      A subsidiary of the British transnational
      corporation Tate & Lyle that ran the cane
      farms and the factories on the Frome and
      Monymusk estates until they were purchased
      by the government.

WORKERS' PARTY OF JAMAICA (WPJ)
      A small, Marxist-Leninist party founded
      during the mid-1970's by Trevor Munroe. Was
      initially called Workers' Liberation League.

APPENDIX III

CHRONOLOGY

JAMAICA AND THE WORLD		SUGAR PLANTATIONS IN JAMAICA	
1509	Spain colonizes Jamaica.		
1517	First African slaves brought to island.		
1655	British take over island.		
		1675	First plantations established.
1725-40	First Maroon wars.		
1795	Second Maroon war.		
1807	Slave trade abolished.		
1815	300,000 slaves, 15,000 whites in Jamaica.	1815	More than 80,000 tons of sugar produced.
1831	Montego Bay slave revolt.		
1838	Slavery abolished.	1838-60	Decline in sugar production; increase in peasant farming.
1900	United Fruit Co. begins dominance of banana industry.		

211

JAMAICA AND THE WORLD	SUGAR PLANTATIONS IN JAMAICA
	1937 WISCO (Tate & Lyle subsidiary) buys major sugar estates.
1938 Island-wide strike. BITU formed by Alexander Bustamante.	1938 Sugar workers join BITU.
1939-45 World War II.	
1950 Foreign aluminum companies begin investing heavily in Jamaican bauxite.	
1962 British grant independence to Jamaica.	
1960's Industrialization-by-invitation development program is embarked upon by JLP government.	1965 Sugar production reaches peak of 500,000 tons.
	1968 JLP government begins discussions with United Fruit and Tate & Lyle on purchase of Frome, Bernard Lodge and Monymusk sugar estates.

212

JAMAICA AND THE WORLD

SUGAR PLANTATIONS IN JAMAICA

1970-71   JLP government buys the three estates with 74,000 acres, including 47,000 acres in cane, sets up Frome Monymusk Land Co which leases cane lands back to Tate & Lyle, and begins negotiations to purchase sugar factories on the three estates.

1972   PNP wins elections: Michael Manley becomes Prime Minister.

1972   Three estate sugar factories sold to government-owned National Sugar Company.

Sept.1972   Manley gives speech about creating cooperatives on government-owned sugar estates.

fall 1972   Father Joseph Owens moves to Lioneltown, near Monymusk estate.

1973   SAC begins organizing sugar workers for cooperatives on the 3 estates.

1973-74   SAC receives grants from Inter-American Foundation for organizing.

213

JAMAICA AND THE WORLD		SUGAR PLANTATIONS IN JAMAICA	
1974	Manley proclaims democratic socialist program; imposes larger bauxite levy.	1974	Frome Monymusk Land Co. begins operating the three estates, taking over from Tate & Lyle.
1974-76	U.S. destabilization campaign to weaken PNP government.	Dec.1974	Three pilot cooperatives begin.
		Aug.1975	Government officials give go-ahead for "second-wave" co-ops at Trelawney Beach Hotel meeting.
Dec.1975	Secretary of State Kissinger visits Jamaica, threatens continued actions against PNP.	Dec.1975	Manley visits Frome. "Bogus Chairmen" episode takes place.
		Dec.1975	Estate and Central Boards of USWCC established.
1976	Carter wins U.S. elections; Manley relected in Jamaica.	Jan.1976	"Second wave" co-ops begin on the three estates. Eight former SAC organizers become Member Service Officers. Workers Time begins publication.

JAMAICA AND THE WORLD

1977   Manley negotiates IMF loan. Jamaican dollar devalued.

SUGAR PLANTATIONS IN JAMAICA

1976   World Bank lends Jamaica U.S. $17 million to renovate 3 estate sugar factories.

Aug.1976   Winston Higgins chosen General Secretary of USWCC by Central Board. Frome Staff Association registered as a trade union.

Sept.1976   Manley speaks near Frome in support of worker participation in sugar factory management.

Dec.1976   Last three farms at Frome become cooperatives.

May 1977   Staff strike at Monymusk & Bernard Lodge.

Jan.1978   Work stoppages at Frome over return of members' severance deposits. Government announces plan for cooperators to borrow up to 2/3 of their severance deposits and postpones return of deposits for three years.

215

SUGAR PLANTATIONS IN JAMAICA

Jan.1978　End of 22-month guaranteed employment of staff with Frome Monymusk Land Co. Beginning of new staff contract with USWCC.

Feb.1978　Island-wide two-week strike by sugar workers in fields and factories.

Apr.1978　Shaw submits report to government on restructuring of co-ops.

Mar.1979　Higgins retires as General Secretary of USWCC; replaced by E.B. Thompson, former chief executive at Frome estate.

May 1979　USWCC receives U.S.$.5 million grant from Inter-American Foundation for education program.

Sept.1979 Lennie Ruddock hired as Director of Education.

JAMAICA AND THE WORLD	SUGAR PLANTATIONS IN JAMAICA
1980 — Reagan elected in U.S.; JLP wins in Jamaica. Edward Seaga becomes Prime Minister.	1980 — Education program begins on 23 cooperative farms.
	Dec.1980 — JLP government officials say they support cooperatives, though this is accompanied by talk of "restructuring".
1981-82 — Seaga negotiates new IMF loans; Jamaican dollar sinks to $.25 U.S.	Jan.1981 — Severance monies due once again. Worker unrest and work stoppages. USWCC unable to meet payroll deduction payments for housing, credit union, etc.
	Summer 1981 — Government-appointed inquirer Anthony Drummond takes testimony at three co-op estates.
	Nov.1981 — JLP government dissolves cooperatives. Barham and 8 other co-op farms appeal.
1983 — U.S. invades Grenada.	

217

JAMAICA AND THE WORLD

1984   Reagan re-elected in U.S.,
JLP continues in power in
Jamaica--unopposed--after
PNP boycotted elections.

1985   Jamaican dollar at all-
time low of US$.20. Riots
and road blocks to protest
increase in gas prices.

SUGAR PLANTATIONS IN JAMAICA

1984   Co-op appeals denied, Sugar
production drops below
200,000 tons.

1985   JLP government awards ten
year management contract to
Tate & Lyle for three estates
and associated sugar factories. Ownership of estates and
factories transferred to
Jamaica Sugar Holdings, Ltd.
to which Tate & Lyle appoints
3 out of 7 directors.

INDEX